Combinatorics
& Probability

Chad Troutwine · Markus Moberg · Chris Kane · Mark Glenn · Denis Sosyura

Co-Founders	**Chad Troutwine**
	Markus Moberg
Managing Editor	**Mark Glenn**
Director of Academic Programs	**Brian Galvin**
Interior Design	**Lisa Johnson**
	Miriam Lubow
Cover Design	**Nick Mason**
	Mike Miller
Contributing Editors	**Megan Kucik**
	Jim Stekelberg
	Guy Guyadeen

A successful educational program is only as good as the people who teach it, and Veritas Prep is fortunate to have many of the world's finest GMAT instructors on its team.

Not only does that team know how to teach a strong curriculum, but it also knows how to help create one. This lesson book would not be possible without the hundreds of suggestions we have received from our talented faculty all across the world – from Seattle, Detroit, and Miami to London, Singapore, and Dubai. Their passion for excellence helped give birth to a new curriculum that is far better than what we could have created on our own.

Our students also deserve a very special thanks. Thousands of them have provided us with something priceless: enthusiastic feedback that has guided us in creating the most comprehensive GMAT preparation course available on the market today.

We therefore dedicate this revised lesson book to all Veritas Prep instructors and students who have tackled the GMAT and given us their valuable input along the way.

Table of Contents

Lesson 12 Introduction

Combinatorics and probability constitute some of the most challenging questions you will see on the Quantitative section of the GMAT. As the Quant scores of test takers have risen in recent years, the test makers have compensated by putting more of these kinds of difficult questions into the test. Only Veritas Prep devotes a whole lesson to these difficult question types. The comprehensive understanding you gain here will enable you to tackle even the most difficult counting and probability problems on test day.

Combinatorics

The term combinatorics refers to an area of mathematics that deals with the arrangements of different items, or permutations and combinations. Some examples of combinatorial problems include calculating the number of different ways to arrange five cards in a row on a table, sit ten people at a corporate reception, or select four elective courses at business school.

Since combinatorics is not covered in a typical high school or college curriculum, these problems are usually classified as upper-bin material. Test-takers aiming at the 90th quantitative percentile will have to correctly solve several problems dealing with combinatorics. As if that was not enough, the test makers often incorporate combinatorial concepts into problems on other topics, especially in probability theory. Despite the increasing prevalence of combinatorics problems, some prep courses still recommend solving them by inspection, i.e. by writing out all possible combinations and counting them. While this approach may yield the desired result, it is very time consuming, prone to error, and difficult to apply to problems with a large number of possibilities and restrictions.

To build the necessary toolkit for solving combinatorics problems quickly and efficiently, this section begins with coverage of the essential theoretical concepts followed by examples and strategies for solving each type of combinatorics problem. This is a difficult lesson and you should not be dismayed if you have trouble understanding everything.

When Does the Order Matter?

Combinatorics problems can be divided into two broad categories — those for which the order of arrangements are important (permutations and basic counting) and those for which the order does not matter (combinations). To provide some insight into these concepts, let's consider a few examples demonstrating the differences between ordered and unordered arrangements.

Permutations

Permutations, or scenarios where the sequence of elements is important, include the arrangement of books on a shelf, finishing order of a race, or numbers in a password when the numbers cannot be repeated. Each variation in the sequence (e.g. switching places of letters, numbers, etc.) will generate a different permutation. If items can be repeated, it is not a true permutation but the order still matters and these can be solved with your understanding of the basic counting principles to be discussed shortly.

Another distinguishing feature of permutations lies in the fact that the number of elements often corresponds to the number of available slots for these elements. Typical problems involving permutations include arranging people in a line (every person needs one slot) or sitting an audience in a movie theatre (each person must be seated).

Combinations

By contrast, questions dealing with combinations (unordered arrangements) refer to arrangements in which the order does not matter and where a smaller group of elements is drawn from a larger pool. Examples of such problems include selecting a three-person case competition team from a class of 250 MBA students, choosing several items from a menu in a student lounge, or purchasing three suits at a department store to wear to your second-round interviews. In each of these cases, the sequence of choices is unimportant and does not create a new combination.

For instance, if students John, Jenny, and Lisa are selected to represent the school at a case competition, changing the order in which they were chosen does not yield a new combination. For instance, a team consisting of Lisa, John, and Jenny selected in that order is the same as the original team where John was selected first, followed by Jenny and Lisa. Similarly, if you order a turkey sandwich, then salad, then a glass of orange juice, you will end up with the same meal, regardless of which item you ordered first.

If the order is not important in combinations, then what is? New combinations are created by selecting a different set of items from the pool of available possibilities. For instance, in our menu example, ordering the same turkey sandwich and a salad with apple juice rather than orange juice would constitute a new combination of a meal. Similarly, replacing any (or all) of the three students with other candidates on the case competition team would also result in a new combination.

Basic Counting Principles

Before you can properly understand the more complicated permutation and combination problems, you must first have a good understanding of the basic concepts surrounding all counting. Many of the counting problems on the GMAT require only this basic understanding of counting and do not require you to differentiate between permutations and combinations. In fact, by using these basic concepts it is often unnecessary to think of counting problems in terms of permutations or combinations. Solving counting problems starts with a basic understanding of the counting tree and counting principles.

Multiply, multiply, multiply…..

Determining the total number of arrangements that are possible in any counting problem starts with multiplication. On many problems you will be summing the number of counts from various cases or dividing to remove repeated sequences, but to determine any individual count you must multiply. Almost all counting problems can be thought of in terms of the number of spots that are available and the number of possibilities for each spot.

Note

There are some permutation and combination problems that cannot be solved with this approach and that require specialized formulas and strategies which we will address later, but most are best solved with this method. Consider a few examples of some problems that can be solved with basic counting principles.

Example: How many lunch combination meals (if you must choose exactly one of each: burger, side, and drink) are possible at a fast food restaurant if you have 3 different burgers to choose from, 3 different drinks to choose from, and 2 different sides to choose from?

Detailed Explanation

To answer any basic counting question, consider the number of spots and the number of possibilities for each spot. Here there are three distinct spots. The first one is for burgers, the second for drinks, and the third for sides. The order that you pick them in is arbitrary (in other words, technically this is a combination but that designation is not important for this type of problem) – just pick one spot for each choice that you have whenever you face a problem such as this and determine the number of choices for each spot.

# of Burger Choices · # of Drink Choices · # of Side Choices = Total # Possible

From the information given in the question, the answer can be calculated easily as $3 \cdot 3 \cdot 2 = 18$ possible combination meals.

To understand why you must multiply consider a basic counting tree, which is a very helpful visual aid.

Facts & Formulas: To determine the number of possible arrangements in most counting problems, simply multiply the number of choices for each available spot in the arrangement.

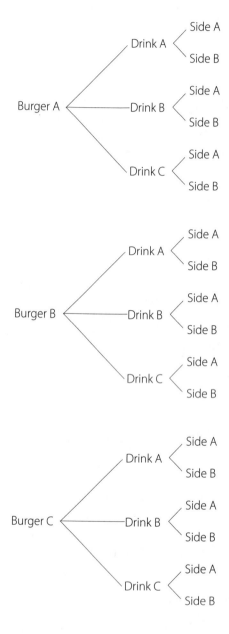

In the upper branch of the tree (Burger A) there are three groups of 2 for a total of 6 possibilities. There are 3 groups because there are three drink choices. Each of these groups is a group of 2 because there are two sidedish choices. Three groups of two = $3 \cdot 2$, so if you choose Burger A, there are 6 possible meals you could order.

Similarly for the lower branches, (Burgers B and C), there are six possible meals for each burger choice. Altogether, there are three groups of six possible meals. There are three groups because there are three types of burgers. Three groups of six = 3 · 6 = 18 total possiblities.

If you were then to be asked if you wanted a dessert and there were four dessert choices (and also the possibility of skipping dessert) there would be 90 total possible meals. For each of the 18 meals already shown in the tree, you could draw five more twigs to represent your dessert choice, so there are 18 groups of five. 18 · 5 = 90, and so on.

Example: *How many license plates are possible if the plate must contain exactly 5 digits (the digits must be in a row and the plate contains no other characters)?*

> *GMAT Insider:* Always ask yourself in a counting question whether items can be repeated. Generally, on actual GMAT questions this information is specified (but not always). The careful test taker is always looking out for these types of "license plate" problems where digits or items can be repeated.

Detailed Explanation
To solve, consider again the number of spots. Here there are 5 different spots and you have 10 choices for each spot (Remember – there are 10 digits: 0 through 9, inclusive). Therefore the answer will be:

$10 \cdot 10 \cdot 10 \cdot 10 \cdot 10 = 10^5 = 100,000$

Obviously, it would take many pages of paper to write out the counting tree for this example, but you can visualize what it would look like and understand that the last row would contain a list 100,000 long. It is also important to note in this problem that the question did not state that the digits cannot be repeated. Therefore you will have 10 choices for each spot. On the GMAT, the problem will generally state that you can or cannot repeat elements, but never make assumptions. In this case it says that each spot must contain a digit, so do not assume that you cannot repeat a digit.

Now let's consider a more difficult example of the same type of problem with different conditions:

Example : *How many license plates are possible if the plate must contain exactly 5 digits and the plate cannot start with zero or repeat any digits (the digits must be in a row and the plate contains no other characters)?*

Detailed Explanation

To solve, use the same methodology. Consider the 5 spots and the number of possibilities for each spot. In this case there are only 9 choices for the first spot because zero is excluded. For the second spot (the tricky part of this problem), you again have 9 possibilities because you cannot repeat the first digit (leaving 8) but zero is now allowed giving us again 9 choices. For the 3rd, 4th and 5th spots, you will have 8, 7, and 6 choices respectively because you lose one choice for each spot. Therefore the answer is as follows:

$$9 \cdot 9 \cdot 8 \cdot 7 \cdot 6 = 81 \cdot 56 \cdot 6 = 27,216$$

Note

If this were an actual GMAT problem, the answer choices would probably allow you to avoid the tedious multiplication above. It is likely that only one answer choice would end in 6, allowing you to use your knowledge of units' digit number properties to answer the question.

Factorials!

Factorials form the basis for calculating permutations and combinations when you cannot use the basic counting strategies discussed previously, so it is essential that students understand the definition of a factorial and the rules that govern them.

What is a factorial? It is a mathematical denotation for the product of all positive integers less than or equal to a specific non-negative integer. For instance, $5! = 5 \cdot 4 \cdot 3 \cdot 2 \cdot 1 = 120$

The table below shows some examples of factorials:

Factorial	Pronounced	Value
3!	Three factorial	$3 \cdot 2 \cdot 1 = 6$
6!	Six factorial	$6 \cdot 5 \cdot 4 \cdot 3 \cdot 2 \cdot 1 = 720$
K!	K factorial	$K \cdot (K-1) \cdot (K-2)...1$

Because N factorial denotes the product of positive integers smaller than or equal to N, negative factorials do not exist. Note that zero factorial is equal to 1, i.e. $0! = 1$.*

Although you can always compute the value of a factorial by writing out the product and multiplying the integers, you may wish to memorize the following factorials that appear frequently on the test:

Common Factorials:

Factorial	Value *
0!	1
1!	1
2!	2
3!	6
4!	24
5!	120
6!	720

Facts & Formulas: The factorial of a number N (denoted N!) is the product of all positive consecutive integers up to N, inclusive: $N! = N \cdot (N-1).....\cdot 2 \cdot 1$

Note
$0! = 1$

*While this is somewhat counter-intuitive, it is derived from the product of empty sets in set theory and is not important to understand.

Beyond memorizing this list and understanding the definition of factorial, students must be efficient at working with factorials in mathematical calculations. Let's consider a few examples:

Solve 3!5!

Solve $\dfrac{8!}{3!5!}$

Detailed Explanations

In the first example note that the answer is NOT 15!. Factorials must be considered individually and cannot be combined in any way. Therefore in the first example the answer is simply $(6)(120) = 720$.

In the second example there is a method that allows you to calculate these values very quickly. Recognize that the calculation can really be considered: $\dfrac{8 \cdot 7 \cdot 6 \cdot 5!}{3!5!}$ The 5 factorials will cancel and you are left with $\dfrac{8 \cdot 7 \cdot 6}{3!}$ Because $3! = 6$ you can see that the answer is 56.

Try this method on a few more examples:

Solve $\dfrac{12!}{3!9!}$

Solve $\dfrac{6!}{2!4!}$

Detailed Explanations

In the first example, the calculation is equivalent to: $\dfrac{12 \cdot 11 \cdot 10 \cdot 9!}{3!9!}$. The 9 factorials will cancel and you are left with $\dfrac{12 \cdot 10 \cdot 11}{3!}$, since 3! = 6 you can see that the answer is $2 \cdot 11 \cdot 10 = 220$. In the second example, the calculation is equivalent to: $\dfrac{6 \cdot 5 \cdot 4!}{2!4!}$. The 4 factorials will cancel and you are left with $\dfrac{6 \cdot 5}{2!} = 15$.

Permutations

As we discussed in the introduction, permutations are arrangements where **order matters**. In a strict mathematical definition, they are also counts where items cannot be reused. Before we look at the formula for permutations, let's look at a simple example of a classic permutation:

Example: In how many ways can 5 students be seated in a row of 5 seats?

Facts & Formulas: In any case when you are determining a permutation where the number of available items (defined as N) equals the number of spots in which to arrange those items (defined as K), the answer is simply N!.

Note
This formula only works in true permutations where items cannot be reused.

Detailed Explanation
This is a classic example of a permutation. Moving people around creates a distinct "arrangement" so order clearly matters and items cannot be reused (once someone is seated, they cannot be placed somewhere else). As with almost all permutations, simply think of it in terms of the basic counting principles introduced previously: There are 5 spots. You have 5 choices of people for the first spot, 4 for the second (once one person is seated he cannot be "reused" in another seat), 3 for the third, 2 for the fourth, and 1 for the last spot (there is no choice for the remaining person once the other 4 people have been seated). Written out it looks like $5 \cdot 4 \cdot 3 \cdot 2 \cdot 1$, which is readily identifiable as 5! or 120. Given this fact, it is clear that this type of permutation is easily shortcut. Students should understand the formula so that they can quickly solve these problems.

Permutations with Selection

Most of the permutations that you will be dealing with on the test involve picking from a larger pool of items (called N) to arrange in a smaller number of spots (called K). In an example such as the previous one, N and K are the same so the answer is simply N!. For permutations where N is bigger than K, you will learn a general formula for all permutations, *but it is generally much easier to solve these problems using the basic counting principles taught previously*. The general permutations formula is more cumbersome to use than the basic counting principles.

To illustrate this point, let's look at an example of a permutation with selection and solve it with basic counting principles. Afterwards you will learn the general formula for all permutations and solve the same problem using that formula.

Example: In how many ways can 6 students be seated in 3 seats?

Detailed Explanation

To solve this question quickly, simply consider the three spots that need to be filled. You have 6 choices for the first spot, 5 choices for the second spot, and 4 choices for the third spot. Therefore the answer is $6 \cdot 5 \cdot 4 = 120$

Let's do the previous example problem using the formula:

Example: *In how many ways can 6 students be seated in 3 seats?*

Facts & Formulas:
General Permutations

In problems where the order of elements is relevant, the elements can't be reused, and N items are to be arranged in K spots, the number of different permutations can be calculated by a formula:
Total number of permutations $= \dfrac{N!}{(N-K)!}$

Note
As you learned previously, when N and K are the same, the result is always N! because (N-K)! will be equal to 1.

N = the number of items to arrange
K = the number of spots in which to arrange those items

Detailed Explanation

To use the formula you must first identify N and K. In this case N = 6 and K = 3. Plugging into the formula you see that the # of possible arrangements $= \dfrac{6!}{(6-3)!} = \dfrac{6!}{3!} = 6 \cdot 5 \cdot 4 = 120$. As you can see, the formula is generally more time consuming than basic counting methods.

Interpreting the Question

Now that you understand basic permutations where N and K are the same and, where N > K, it is important to focus on the interpretation of questions. Interpreting the question properly is one of the most important skills on all counting and probability questions. Let's look at a couple more examples of basic permutation questions on the following page, to make sure you are interpreting this type properly.

Examples:

1. In how many ways can 5 different vases be arranged in a row on a mantle?

2. How many different 2 letter codes are possible, if the letters cannot be repeated?

3. How many 3-digit passwords are possible on a home security system keypad that consists of all the digits?

4. In how many ways can 5 people be seated at a circular table?

> *Lazy Genius:* Most people are taught to do permutations like those in number 2 with the general formula for permutations. The formula is always more cumbersome than using basic counting principles, but elements of it are used in other important formulas so it should be understood.

Detailed Explanations

1. Here you are arranging 5 vases in 5 spots where order matters and items cannot be reused. It is therefore a simple permutation where N = K so the answer is simply N! = 5! = 120.

2. Because the letters cannot be repeated, you must consider the number of choices for each of two spots: 26 for the first and 25 for the second. Thus the answer using basic counting principles is 26 · 25. To solve quickly, remember your calculation shortcuts: 25^2 = 625, so 26 · 25 = 625 + 25 = 650. If you solve this with the permutations formula the answer looks like this as N = 26 and K = 2:

# of arrangements $= \dfrac{26!}{(26-2)!} = \dfrac{26!}{24!} = 26 \cdot 25 = 650$

3. For this question you must ask: is it a true permutation or not? While a question on the GMAT will probably specify it (although it is not always clarified for you), this question does not specify that you cannot repeat digits. As a result it is not a true permutation and you cannot use the permutations formula. As always, however, you can use you basic counting principles to see that there are 10 choices for each of the three spots. Therefore the answer is 10 · 10 · 10 = 10^3 and 1000 3 digit codes are possible.

4. In circular permutations, the starting point is arbitrary so there are not as many distinct arrangements for a certain number of elements as when they are in a row. In this example consider five people: A, B, C, D, E. In a line, ABCDE is a distinct arrangement from BCDEA. However, if you draw them in a circle you cannot differentiate between those two arrangements – they are considered the same. In order to count arrangements in a circle, simply fix one spot and then see how many ways the elements can be arranged that are remaining. In this case fix A, and you can arrange B, C, D, and E in 4! ways. Put in a simple formula, circular arrangements of N items = (N – 1)!

> *Facts & Formulas:* If a question asks for the number of different arrangements of x elements, when those elements are arranged in a circle, use the following formula: (x - 1)!

Let's examine two GMAT questions on basic permutations and then move on to some more difficult question types

1.   Bill is renting DVDs from the video store. He must choose 3 DVDs from a list of 8 new releases and then decide in what order to watch them. How many different schedules of videos can he create, if he cannot watch the same movie more than once?

(A)   24

(B)   56

(C)   72

(D)   336

(E)   512

2.   There is a set of 10 letters: A, B, C, D, E, F, G, H, I, J. There are 5 character and 4 character codes to be made out of these letters. Each of the codes can use any of the 10 letters without repeating them in any one code. What is the ratio of the total number of possible 5 character codes to the number of possible 4 character codes?

(A)   1 : 6

(B)   1 : 5

(C)   5 : 1

(D)   6 : 1

(E)   10 : 1

Permutations with Repeating Elements

In all of our examples so far, we have been ordering distinct items: people or things that are not identical. However, there are counting problems where you are asked to give the number of arrangements for a group of items in which some things are identical. Examples of these problems include computing the number of arrangements of 5 pens in a row, two of which are identical, or finding the number of different arrangements that can be created with a set of letters, where some letters are the same.

These are true permutations because you are not reusing items but the number of possible different arrangements is reduced because some of the items are the same. If all of the N items were distinct, the number of different orderings would be N! However, since some of the N items are the same, the opportunities to create new orderings are reduced by the number of permutations that could be created from the identical items. Let's look at a simple example to highlight this fact:
In how many ways can you arrange the three letters A, B, and C?

Clearly the answer is 3!, but let's write them out so you can see the different arrangements:

ABC
ACB
BAC
BCA
CAB
CBA

Now consider the same question if we replace the C with another B and ask:
In how many ways can you arrange the three letters A, B, B?

Now the arrangements look like this:

ABB
ABB
BAB
BBA
BAB
BBA

As you can see, there are now only 3 distinct arrangements because the identical element creates repeating arrangements that cannot be counted separately.

> *How Your Mind Works:* If you forget your basic combinatorics and formulas, it is possible on easier problems to write out the combinations and permutations. Writing them out is more time-consuming, but if you must do so, be methodical so that you don't forget any possibilities. First write out all the possibilities starting with A, then all those starting with B, etc.

While writing out the possibilities works in a simple example such as this, it will not work for most problems. There is a formula for dealing with all permutations with repeating elements that must be memorized.

Formula for Permutations with Repeating Elements

The number of arrangements of N elements where certain elements are repeated is represented by the formula: $\frac{N!}{A!B!...}$ where N is the number of items being arranged and each factorial in the denominator represents an item that is repeated and the variable represents the number of times the item repeats.

Example: Consider our simple example of arranging the letters A, B, and B. Here we have three items so N = 3 and we have one item that repeats 2 times. Therefore, the answer is $\frac{3!}{2!} = 3$

Note
You will only be given permutation questions with repeating elements if N and K are the same. You will not be asked to do permutations with selection and repeating elements unless it is easily written out. The preceding formula is only for problems where N and K are the same.

Example: In how many ways can the letters of Mississippi be arranged in a row?

Detailed Explanation

Using the formula, we establish N as 11 and then we look for how many items repeat. In this case there are three items that repeat – *i*, *s*, and *p*. The *i* repeats 4 times, the *s* repeats 4 times, and the *p* repeats 2 times. So the formula will look like this: $\frac{11!}{4!4!2!}$. Although it is unlikely that you will have to do such a lengthy calculation on the test, by solving with the methods discussed previously you see that the answer is $\frac{11 \cdot 10 \cdot 9 \cdot 8 \cdot 7 \cdot 6 \cdot 5}{4 \cdot 3 \cdot 2 \cdot 2}$ after canceling one of the 4 factorials in the numerator and denominator. This leaves you with $1000 \cdot 35 - (10 \cdot 35) = 35,000 - 350 = 34,650$ ways.

Let's do a couple of complete problems to ingrain this formula and see how it is tested on the GMAT:

3. Cliff is contemplating a name for a new sailboat that he recently purchased. He has a set of copper letters from the word PEPPER left from the name of his earlier sailboat, and plans to use all of them for his new boat. If he can use only the letters from the previous boat, how many different names can he create, assuming that a name of the boat does not necessarily have to be a meaningful word?

(A)   6

(B)   60

(C)   120

(D)   360

(E)   72

4. There are 4 identical copies each of 5 different magazines. In how many ways can the magazines be arranged in a row on a shelf, if nothing else is arranged with them?

(A) $\frac{5!}{4!}$

(B) $\frac{5!}{(4!)^5}$

(C) $\frac{20!}{(5!)^4}$

(D) $\frac{20!}{(4!)^5}$

(E) $\frac{20!}{5(4!)}$

Permutations Where K is Changing

Another very common type of permutation problem is one where you must consider numerous values for K and then sum together the results. These are typically indicated by the trigger words "At least", "At most", and "Or". Consider the following example:

Example: Anna has to visit at least 2 European cities on her vacation trip. If she can visit only London, Paris, Rome, or Madrid, how many different itineraries, defined as the sequence of visited cities, can Anna create if she cannot visit the same city twice?

> *Lazy Genius:* In any permutation, when K = N and K = N - 1 the number of arrangements will always be the same (in this case 24). This information allows you to shortcut calculations on problems such as this and solve them quickly.

Detailed Explanation

In problems such as this look for key language such as "at least", "at most", and "or". Here you see that there will be multiple values for K because it says "at least 2" cities. There are 4 cities to choose from and Anna can visit 2, 3, or 4 different cities. Every 2 city itinerary is unique from every 3 city itinerary and every 4 city itinerary, and vice versa. In other words, going to Paris, Rome, and Madrid is necessarily a different itinerary from Paris, Rome, Madrid, and London.

To solve this problem you have to solve for each of the three cases and then sum them together:

N = 4 (4 Cities to choose from)

	Using Basic Counting	Using Formula
K = 4	$4 \cdot 3 \cdot 2 \cdot 1 = 4! = 24$	$\frac{4!}{(4-4)!} = \frac{4!}{0!} = 4! = 24$
K = 3	$4 \cdot 3 \cdot 2 = 24$	$\frac{4!}{(4-3)!} = \frac{4!}{1!} = 4! = 24$
K = 2	$4 \cdot 3 = 12$	$\frac{4!}{(4-2)!} = \frac{4!}{2!} = \frac{24}{2} = 12$

Sum of all unique itineraries = 60

Let's look at two problems to ingrain this concept:

5.   Mike, a DJ at a high-school radio station, needs to play two or three more songs before the end of the school dance. If each composition must be selected from a list of the 10 most popular songs of the year, how many song sequences are available for the remainder of the dance if the songs cannot be repeated?

(A)   6

(B)   90

(C)   120

(D)   720

(E)   810

6.   A company assigns product codes consisting of all the letters in the alphabet. How many product codes are possible if the company uses at most 3 letters in its codes, and all letters can be repeated in any one code?

(A)   15,600

(B)   16,226

(C)   17,576

(D)   18,278

(E)   28,572

Permutations with Restrictions

The hardest types of counting problems are those with particular restrictions or constraints. These problems are relatively uncommon on the GMAT but they appear with enough regularity that students should be prepared for them. There are no special formulas for these problems, but they do require certain approaches to solve them effectively. For most restriction problems, once you have seen a certain type you will not be fooled by it again. Let's start with an example problem and then discuss how to approach these difficult problems:

Example: *John and 4 friends go to a Lakers game. In how many ways can they be seated in 5 consecutive seats, if John has to sit between 2 friends?*

Detailed Explanation
In approaching restriction problems, there are always two ways to attack them:

1. Add up all the ways that are allowed by the restriction,

                          OR

2. Get the total without any restrictions and then subtract the number of ways that break the restriction.

On certain problems adding up the allowed arrangements is faster and on others subtracting out the prohibited arrangements will be faster. As a result, you should be comfortable with both approaches.

In this example it does not matter which approach you use so let's do it first by adding up all the ways that are allowed by the restriction. If John must sit between 2 friends, then he can sit in the 2nd, 3rd, or 4th seats. To think about it properly, put John in the 2nd seat and then consider how many ways everyone can be seated around him in that case:

Alex   John   Bill   Cindy   Dan

With John fixed, you can see that the four people (A, B, C, D) can be arranged 4 factorial ways around him. So with John in the second seat, there are 4! or 24 possible seating arrangements. Taking this to the next logical step, you see that there are 24 seating arrangements for each of the 5 seats that John could sit in. Because he is allowed to sit in 3 of the 5 seats you can simply sum the allowed arrangements for each case. In this case it is $24 + 24 + 24$ or $3 \cdot 24 = 72$ ways.

The other approach would be to consider all the ways the friends could be seated if there were no restrictions. In this case that is 5! or 120 ways. John is not allowed to sit on either of the end seats so if you subtract out the number of ways that break the restriction from 120 then you will also get the answer. Of the 120 possible ways, 24 of them have John in the first seat and 24 of them have him in the last seat. Subtracting 48 from 120 you come up with the same answer of 72 ways. An even quicker way to utilize this approach would be to realize that because John is barred from 2 out of 5 seats, $\frac{2}{5}$ of the permutations are not allowed. Thus the number of permutations with restrictions is $\frac{3}{5}$ the number of permutations without restrictions. $\frac{3}{5}(120) = 72$.

Common Restriction Problems

In the drill section and homework problems you will be exposed to the following common restriction problems, which are all approached with a similar method:

1. Circular arrangements

2. Couples or groups that must sit together

3. Alternating seating (boy, girl, etc.)

4. Limited seating (John must sit between two friends)

GMAT Insider:
To solve constrained counting problems, use one of the two approaches:

1. Solve the problem without the constraint and exclude the cases that do not satisfy the constraint.

———————————

OR

———————————

2. Consider only the scenarios that meet the constraints and sum up the total number of possibilities for each of the scenarios.

Combinations

In the previous section we considered situations when the order of elements was important — changing the order of items resulted in a new arrangement. In another large class of problems, the order of items is irrelevant. Some of these situations include selecting a committee of 5 members from 10 nominees, choosing 3 office locations from 7 major cities, or allocating 4 job offers among 10 interviewees. In each of these cases, mere rearrangement of the elements (i.e. a change in the sequence in which the committee members are selected or job offers extended) does not create a new combination. Therefore, the order in which the elements are arranged is unimportant.

For instance, if job offers were extended to Lisa, Mark, Lena, and Terry in that sequence, changing the order in which the job offers were extended, (e.g. to Mark, Lisa, Terry, and Lena) will not result in a new group of hires. The only way to create a new combination would be to add, drop, or replace one or more of the selected elements. For example, if 4 offers have to be extended, a new combination of recruits can be created by extending an offer to, say, Frank rather than Mark.

Because rearranging the elements in questions where the order is irrelevant will not create a new combination, all combination problems deal with selecting a smaller subset from a larger pool. Otherwise, if all elements from the pool have to be included in the selection and the order of items is unimportant, there is only one way to make this choice. For instance, there is only one way to select a group of 5 new hires from 5 interviewees or to choose a team of 8 participants from 8 nominees. No additional combinations can be created.

Combinatorics Drill
State which of the following are permutations and which are combinations:

> *How Your Mind Works:* If you are confused about whether a counting problem is a combination or a permutation, ask yourself the following question:
> *If I change the order would the new arrangement be considered distinct?*

1. How many different collections of 4 books can Mary take on vacation if she has 20 books to choose from?

2. In how many ways can 20 books be arranged on a shelf?

3. At a race, how many different orderings are possible for 1st, 2nd, and 3rd place if the race has 20 participants?

4. How many subcommittees of 4 are possible from a committee of 12 people?

Now let's look at the formula that is required to solve most combinations:

$$\frac{N!}{K! \cdot (N-K)!}$$

Note

This expression is quite similar to the permutations formula. The only difference is that K! appears in the denominator of the combinations formula and thus reduces the resulting number of total arrangements. The intuition behind this difference is that the number of ordered arrangements created from a pool of elements has to be greater than or equal to the number of unordered arrangements. If a mere rearrangement of the items yields a new variation, we can create far more new arrangements than in the case when the order of items is irrelevant. Therefore, for a given size of the pool and number of elements in the selection, the number of possible permutations (ordered arrangements) will always be greater than or equal to the number of combinations (unordered arrangements).

> **Facts & Formulas:** Combinations
> The number of unordered arrangements consisting of K items selected from a pool of N elements is computed from the Combinations Formula.
>
> Number of unordered arrangements
> $$= \frac{N!}{K! \cdot (N-K)!}$$

Let's look at an example problem and apply the formula from the top of the page:

Example: *Jose needs to select 3 other people for his study group in a core finance class. If there are 8 other students in the class still seeking a group, in how many ways can he form his group?*

> **GMAT Insider:** Combination Problems where K is greater than one require the use of the combinations formula. Along with permutations with repeating elements, they are the only counting problems on the GMAT that require memorization of a formula and cannot be easily solved with the basic counting principles discussed in the opening section. It is essential that students are comfortable working with this formula.

Detailed Explanation

When solving combinations such as this, you simply plug values into the formula and get

the number of arrangements. Here N = 8 and K = 3 so the solution is:

$$\frac{8!}{3!(8-3)!} = \frac{8!}{3!5!} = \frac{8 \cdot 7 \cdot 6}{6} = 56 \text{ ways to arrange the groups.}$$

Let's take our understanding of basic combinations and apply it to a more complex combination problem that has been very common on the GMAT:

7.   At a high school track tryout, there are 8 women and 5 men competing for the 3 male and 3 female spots on the decathlon team. How many different combinations of decathletes are possible on the final team for the six spots?

(A)   112, 896

(B)   3,136

(C)   560

(D)   66

(E)   18

Combinations Where K is Changing

Just as with permutations, combination problems can involve scenarios where K is changing and you must sum up multiple counts. Again look for the key trigger words such as "At least", "At most" and "Or". The key is to do it as fast as possible as these problems can appear tedious. As you will see in the explanation, there are some helpful shortcuts. Consider the following example:

Example: *A child throws six differently colored M&Ms up in the air. How many different possible groups of at least one M&M are there that she could catch in her mouth?*

Detailed Explanation

This is a classic combination problem because the order that they fall into her mouth is not relevant. In this case you see that N = 6 but K could be any value from 1 to 6. As with the permutation example, you need to sum together the results from all different K values. Do not use the formula unless it is necessary (although it will be shown for each one)

For each calculation N = 6

K = 6   There is only one way to catch all 6:

$$\frac{6!}{6!(6-6)!} = \frac{6!}{6!0!} = 1$$

K = 5   If you are catching 5 in your mouth then 1 is falling on the ground. It should be evident that there 6 ways for each color to fall individually on the ground and be left out:

$$\frac{6!}{5!(6-5)!} = \frac{6!}{5!1!} = 6$$

K = 4   Use formula: $\frac{6!}{4!(6-4)!} = \frac{6!}{4!2!} = \frac{6 \cdot 5}{2} = 15$

K = 3   Use formula: $\frac{6!}{3!(6-3)!} = \frac{6!}{3!3!} = \frac{6 \cdot 5 \cdot 4}{6} = 20$

> *How Your Mind Works:* She is not going to catch 1 M&M And 2 M&Ms And 3 M&Ms... She is going to catch 1 M&M Or 2 M&Ms Or 3 M&Ms. When you think "or" you add. When you think "and" you multiply.

K = 2   Same as K = 4

Remember catching 2 in your mouth and having 4 hit the ground must be the same as catching 4 in your mouth and having 2 hit the ground.

The formula shows this: $\frac{6!}{2!(6-2)!} = \frac{6!}{2!4!} = \frac{6 \cdot 5}{2} = 15$

K = 1   Same as K = 5 $\frac{6!}{1!(6-1)!} = \frac{6!}{1!5!} = 6$

Total = 1 + 6 + 15 + 20 + 15 + 6 = 63 different combinations are possible.

Note

While this problem seems tedious you really only need to do 2 combination calculations: when K = 4 and K = 3. All the other ones are repeated or can be deduced without the formula.

Combinations with Restrictions

Combinations with restrictions are approached in the same manner as permutations with restrictions. For most students, however, they are conceptually more difficult and account for some of the hardest counting questions possible on the GMAT. For most combinations with restrictions, it is faster to find the arrangements that break the restriction and subtract them from the number of possibilities without any restrictions. Consider the following problem.

Example: A committee of 4 is to be chosen from 7 employees for a special project at ACME Corporation. 2 of the 7 employees are unwilling to work with each other. How many committees are possible if the 2 employees do not work together?

Detailed Explanation

If there were no restrictions, then it would be a relatively easy combination problem. $N = 7$ and $K = 4$ so the number of arrangements is: $\frac{7!}{4!(7-4)!} = \frac{7!}{4!3!} = \frac{7 \cdot 6 \cdot 5}{6} = 35$. However, some of those groups are not allowed because they would contain the two employees that won't work together. To figure out exactly how many of these 35 are not allowed, imagine the two people together as a single unit and then see how many ways you can fill the remaining 2 spots. Since the two "enemy" employees are already grouped together as one, there are 5 people left to fill the 2 remaining spots. This is a simple combination when $N = 5$ and $K = 2$ which is: $\frac{5!}{2!(5-2)!} = \frac{5!}{2!3!} = \frac{5 \cdot 4}{2} = 10$. So, of the 35 ways to make a committee of 4 from 7 people, 10 of them have the 2 enemy employees together and must be eliminated. That leaves 25 possible committees with the restriction given in the problem. REMEMBER – To solve a problem like this, group the "enemies" together as a single unit, see how many ways they can break the restriction, and subtract that from the total. While this problem can be solved by adding up all the ways that are allowed, it is much more tedious and prone to error.

Review Strategies for Approaching Counting Problems

1. Interpret the question properly and pick an approach.

The first, most important step in a counting problem is to properly interpret the question.

- First, decide if you can solve it by using the basic counting principles discussed in the beginning of this section.

- If you can designate the number of spots and the number of choices for each spot, simply multiply the results for the answer.

- If it is a small number of items, you may also want to write out all the possibilities.

- If the question is a more complex combination or a permutation with identical elements, you will need to apply some of the formulas introduced previously.

- In order to properly interpret the problem and pick an approach, you should go through the following decision paths in your mind.

2. Combinatorics Decision Paths

This strategy will provide a framework that you can apply to the majority of counting problems and will help you structure your approach, determine the appropriate formulas, and apply all necessary strategies. In many cases, it is difficult to get started on a challenging combinatorics problem. This framework will provide you with a way to begin your analysis and narrow down the number of approaches to the problem. The Decision Paths as such do not need to be memorized, but it is in your best interest to be familiar enough with them so that they come naturally by test day. To deconstruct a test problem, apply a series of standard questions:

1. Does changing the order of elements create a new arrangement?

If yes,
the order is important and we are dealing with permutations; proceed with path A.

If no,
the order is irrelevant and we are dealing with combinations; proceed with path B.

Path A (Permutations)

A1. Are items allowed to be repeated?

If yes,
then think of the license plate problem and use basic counting principles.

If no,
use the same basic counting principles or the permutations formula: N!/(N-K)!

A2. Are any of the elements identical?

If yes,
use the formula for permutations with repeating elements: $\frac{N!}{A!B!...}$

If no,
use the basic counting principles or the general permutations formula to solve with the given values for N and K.

A3. Is K changing in the problem?

Look for trigger words such as "At least", "At most" and "or" to see if you need to consider multiple values for K.

If K is changing in the problem, sum up all the results for the different values of K given one value for N.

A4. Are there any additional constraints in the problem?

If yes,
Either (1) adjust your results to account for the scenarios that do not satisfy the constraints and get the final answer or (2) add up all the scenarios that do satisfy the constraints.

If no,
check whether you have considered all possible cases and select the final answer.

Path B (Combinations)

B1. Is K changing or are you putting together multiple combinations?

If yes,
then make sure you solve the various cases individually, and then decide whether to add ("or") or multiply ("and").

If no,
then simply apply the basic combination formula and look for constraints: $\dfrac{N!}{K! \cdot (N-K)!}$

B2. Are there any additional constraints in the problem?

If yes, calculate the number of combinations from the combinations formula and adjust your results according to the constraints (subtract senarios that don't fit the constraints or include senarios that do fit the constraints); then select the final answer.

If no, apply the combinations formula, check whether you have considered all scenarios, and select the final answer.

Note
For additional practice with advanced restrictions problems, see the Counting Drill at the end of the lesson.

> *Habits of Great Test Takers*: The only real scarcity on the GMAT is time. That's it. If it weren't for the time constraints, most people would do incredibly well on the GMAT. Therefore, your advantage will not be to know how to do long division, or decimal multiplication, or interger factoring. Everyone can do that. Your advantage will be to do them faster and more efficiently than the next person. Be on the constant lookout for ways to simplify problems and cut through the GMAT's "smoke and mirrors".
> — Aaron Pond, SALT LAKE CITY

Combinatorics Summary

1. Concepts and Formulas

Basic Counting Principle — to determine the total number of possible arrangements always multiply the number of possible choices for each available spot.

Factorial — a product of all positive consecutive integers less than or equal to the number under the factorial.

Examples: $N! = N \cdot (N-1) \ldots \cdot 2 \cdot 1$ $9! = 9 \cdot 8 \cdot 7 \cdot 6 \cdot 5 \cdot 4 \cdot 3 \cdot 2 \cdot 1 = 362{,}880$

Permutations — ordered arrangements of elements without repetition.

Examples:
(1)   Letters in a password (without repetition)

(2)   Arrangements of 5 students in 5 seats

Number of ways to arrange N distinct items in N spots = N!

Permutations with repeating elements — permutations of elements, some of which are indistinguishable from others.

Examples:
(1)   Arrangements of different vases, two of which are identical

(2)   Arrangements of letters, some of which are repeated

Number of arrangements of N items, of which A,B... are the same $= \dfrac{N!}{A!B!\ldots}$

General Permutations Formula:

Number of ordered K-element arrangements created from N elements $= \dfrac{N!}{(N-K)!}$

Combinations — unordered arrangements of elements.

Examples: Members or a committee or students in a study group

General Combinations Formula:

Number of unordered K-element sets created from N elements $= \dfrac{N!}{K! \cdot (N-K)!}$

Note
Combinations and Permutations can be notated in the following manner:

$_NC_K$ for combinations and $_NP_K$ for permutations. $_8C_3$ stands for a combination where N = 8 and K = 3 and $_8P_5$ stands for a permutation where N = 8 and K = 5. You will not see this denotation on the test but it is used often in the homework explanations.

2. Strategies and Tips

- Whenever possible, use the basic principles of counting to solve with the number of choices for each available spot. This method can be used for all problems except permutations with repeating elements and group combinations.

- To distinguish between combinations and permutations, try to change the order of the items. If this change yields a new arrangement, apply the formulas for permutations; otherwise, use the formulas for combinations.

- Write out problems involving a limited number of elements.

- To structure your approach to combinatorics problems, use the Combinatorics Decision Tree.

- When performing computations with factorials, write out the products of integers and reduce similar terms before performing other operations.

- The number of ways to select at least or at most K elements can be found by computing the number of ways to select each allowable number of elements, i.e. ways to select K, K + 1, ..., N elements for "at least problems" and 1, 2, ..., K elements for "at most" problems.

- To solve constrained combinatorics problems, use one of two approaches:

  (1)   Solve the problem without the constraint and exclude the cases that do not satisfy the constraint.
          OR
  (2)   Consider only the scenarios that meet the constraints and sum up the total number of possibilities for each of the scenarios.

Probability Beating the Odds

The concept of probability refers to the likelihood of the occurrence of a certain event. This likelihood can be measured in percents, decimals, or fractions. If the event is certain to occur, its probability is said to be 1 (or 100%). For example, if you draw a ball from an jar that contains only white balls, the probability that this ball is white is 100% or simply 1. On the other hand, if the event cannot occur under the current circumstances, the probability of its occurrence is zero. Considering our example of a ball from an jar of white balls, the probability that this ball is black is zero because there were no black balls in the jar.

These two extreme cases denote boundaries for the values of probability — the minimum value of 0 and the maximum value of 1. The entire spectrum of probabilities of any event falls between 0 and 1, inclusive.

All probability values lie between 0 and 1, or between 0% and 100%, inclusive.

Probability of a Single Event

The probability of a single event is determined by the ratio of the outcomes when this event occurs to the total number of possible outcomes. This is commonly described as favorable outcomes over total outcomes. For example, when you make a blind guess on a GMAT question, you have a total of 5 outcomes (choices A through E) but only one favorable outcome. Thus, the likelihood of answering any GMAT question correctly based on a blind guess is one out of five (1/5) or 0.2 or 20%. The probability of an event A is calculated as follows:

$$P(A) = \frac{\text{\# of outcomes when A occurs}}{\text{\# of possible outcomes}}$$

Questions dealing with the probability of a single event are generally straightforward from a probability standpoint, but questions involving multiple events become much more complicated. Before we can deal with those types of questions you must understand several important concepts and definitions.

Important Definitions

1. Mutually Exclusive Events

Understanding the concept of mutually exclusive events is very important for working with the general case formula for probability to which you will be introduced shortly. Two events are called **mutually exclusive** if they can never occur together, i.e. occurrence of one event completely eliminates the probability of occurrence of the other.

Examples of mutually exclusive events:

- *Getting a 750 and a 730 on the same GMAT test.*
- *The Yankees and the Red Sox winning the World Series in the same year.*
- *Getting a head and a tail on one flip of a coin*
- *Winning and coming in second in the Boston Marathon in the same year.*

If events A and B are mutually exclusive, **P(A and B) = 0.**

2. Complementary Events

Events are called **complementary** if one and only one of them must occur. Since only one of the complementary events can occur, all complementary events are mutually exclusive. In other words, events complement one another if one or the other must occur, but they can never occur together. As a result, the sum of the probabilities of complementary events always equals 1.

Events A and B are complementary if one and only one of them **must** occur.

Examples of complementary events:

- *Getting a heads or tails on a flip of a coin*
- *Getting a speeding ticket or not getting a speeding ticket on the way home from class.*
- *Getting into Harvard Business School or not getting into Harvard Business School.*
- *Getting at least one tail on 3 flips of a coin or getting no tails*

Facts & Formulas:
Complementary events are necessarily mutually exclusive: **P(A and B) = 0.**

The sum of the probabilities of complementary events is always 1: **P(A or B) = 1.**

As you will see shortly, understanding complementary events is an essential skill for many GMAT probability questions. Consider the following example:

Example: On a probability midterm, John has an 82% chance of getting at least one problem correct. What is the probability that he gets none of the problems correct?

> **GMAT Insider:** Whenever you are dealing with complementary events, you can always determine the probability of one complementary event by subtracting the probability of the other complementary event from one. Often it is much easier to find the probability of one of the two complementary events. Always find the probability of the event that is easier to determine and then simply subtract it from one to determine the probability of the complementary event.

Detailed Explanation

On this example and on many difficult GMAT problems, you must identify that you are dealing with complementary events. In this case, getting at least one correct and getting none correct are complementary events. One and only one of those two scenarios must take place and therefore the sum of the probabilities must equal one. If John has an 82% chance of getting at least one question correct, he must have an 18% chance of getting none correct.

3. Independent Events

Events A and B are **independent** if the occurrence of one event does not affect the probability of the occurrence of another. In the case of sequential events, the initial probability is restored before each subsequent event.

Examples of independent events:

- *Flips of a coin*
- *Rolls of a die*
- *Winning the lottery and getting struck by lightning*
- *Picking balls out of an jar with replacement*

4. Dependent Events

Events A and B are **dependent** if the occurrence of one event affects the probability of another. In calculating the probability of multiple events that are dependent on each other, the probability will change with each event.

Examples of dependent events:

- *Picking balls out of an jar without replacement*
- *Picking cards out of a deck without replacement*

Example : There are 6 blue marbles and 3 red marbles in a bowl. 2 blue marbles are removed. What is the probability of picking a blue marble?

Detailed Explanation

Most dependent probability problems on the GMAT involve balls in an jar or cards in a deck because they are good examples of dependent or "conditional" probability. In this example you do not have to calculate multiple probabilities, but you do have to consider the probability of one pick after certain actions. The original probability of picking a blue marble before the change was $\frac{6}{9}$ or $\frac{2}{3}$. After removing 2 blue marbles there are now 7 total marbles, of which 4 are favorable. Therefore, the probability of picking a blue marble after the initial removal is $\frac{4}{7}$.

Probability of One Event <u>AND</u> Another

1. Independent events

When determining the probability of multiple independent events, simply multiply the individual probabilities. Consider the following example:

Example: If the probability of winning the lottery is one in a million, and the probability of getting struck by lightning is one in a million, what is the probability that Bill wins the lottery and gets struck by lightning on the same day?

Detailed Explanation

When determining the probability of one event AND another event, multiply the two probabilities together. In this example, the probability of one event has nothing to do with the other event, so they are independent events. This simplifies the problem and allows you to simply multiply the individual probabilities: $\frac{1}{10^6} \cdot \frac{1}{10^6} = \frac{1}{10^{12}}$.

Therefore, the probability of both events taking place is one in a trillion.

More examples of multiple independent events:

Facts & Formulas:
For independent events A and B, the probability of both events occurring is the product of the probabilities of the two events: $P(A \text{ and } B) = P(A) \cdot P(B)$

1. What is the probability of rolling 3 sixes in a row on three rolls of a fair six sided die?

2. What is the probability of getting 4 heads in a row on 4 flips of a coin?

3. What is the probability of getting a 3 heads in a row and then a tail on 4 flips of a coin?

4. A jar contains 2 black balls and 3 red balls. What is the probability of picking a black ball and then another black ball, if the balls are replaced between the two picks?

2. Dependent Events

When determining the probability of multiple dependent events, multiply the probability of the first event times the probability of the second event assuming the first event has occurred. Consider the following example:

Example: *There are 4 black balls and 3 white balls in an jar. What is the probability of picking one black ball AND then one white ball, without replacement?*

Detailed Explanation

As with independent events, you need to multiply the probability of the two events.

However, in this case the probability of the second event is dependent on the first event.

For the first event, the probability is $\frac{4}{7}$. For the second event, the probability has changed based upon the first event. Since one ball has been taken out, there are now six total outcomes and, assuming that the ball picked was black, three of them are favorable.

Therefore, the probability of picking a white ball on the second pick is $\frac{3}{6} = \frac{1}{2}$. The probability of the two events is thus $\frac{4}{7} \cdot \frac{1}{2} = \frac{2}{7}$.

Combinatorics & Probability

Events A and B are **dependent** if the occurrence of one event affects the probability of another.

3. Probability of Simultaneous Events

One very confusing type of GMAT problem for students is when you are asked to pick two balls from a jar at the same time or two cards from the deck at the same time. Consider this example question:

Example: A jar contains 4 black and 3 white balls. If you reach into the jar and pick two balls at the same time, what is the probability that one ball is black and one is white?

Facts & Formulas: The probability of dependent events occurring together is calculated using the general-case AND formula: **P(A and B) = P(A) • P_A(B)** Here P(A and B) is the probability that both these events will occur; P(A) is the probability of event A; P_A(B) is the probability that event B will occur assuming that A has already occurred; P_A(B) is called conditional probability.

How Your Mind Works: In dealing with dependent or "conditional" probability problems, do not forget to properly adjust the probability of the second event dependent on the first. To adjust the probability properly, remember to change both the favorable outcomes AND the total outcomes. The common error that students make is to forget to reduce the number of total outcomes.

Detailed Explanation

Any question in probability that asks you to calculate the probability of two things happening simultaneously is really asking you to do it one at a time, without replacement. In this question, rephrase it as the following: what is the probability of picking a black ball and then a white ball without replacement? The proof that "at the same time" and "one at a time without replacement" are the same question lies in the fact that the order in which you pick the two balls without replacement will never matter. Consider the probability of picking black and then white: $\frac{4}{7} \cdot \frac{3}{6} = \frac{2}{7}$. This probability will always be the same as picking white and then black: $\frac{3}{7} \cdot \frac{4}{6} = \frac{2}{7}$. Conceptually, many people are confused by this fact, but the mathematics proves it conclusively.

Let's examine two difficult "simultaneous" questions that you will solve later in the lesson:

1. What is the probability of picking two cards off the top of a deck of cards and getting a pair?

How you should think about the question: What is the probability of picking one card and then the next and getting a pair, if the cards are not replaced?

2. What is the probability of getting at least one pair if four fair six sided dice are rolled simultaneously?

How you should think about the question: What is the probability of getting at least one pair in four rolls of a fair six sided die, one after another?

> *GMAT Insider:* Any question that asks for the probability of two events simultaneously can and should be thought of as "one at a time, without replacement." If the problem involves dependent events, make the calculations accordingly. If the problem involves independent events, just multiply the fixed probability.

Probability of One Event <u>OR</u> Another

In the previous examples we were dealing with the probability of multiple events – of one event AND another. What happens, however, when you are asked for one event OR another? Let's return to the lottery and lightning example and rephrase the question:

Example: *If the probability of winning the lottery is one in a million, and the probability of getting struck by lightning is one in a million, what is the probability that Bill wins the lottery OR gets struck by lightning on the same day?*

Detailed Explanation

The original example was asking for the probability of one event and another, so the resulting probability was astronomically unlikely ($\frac{1}{10^6} \cdot \frac{1}{10^6}$). However, when the question is asking for the probability of one event OR another, that probability must be greater than the probability of either event alone (unless the individual probabilities are each 0 or 1, in which case the resulting OR probability would be the same). To calculate this probability you must use the general case formula for probability:

$$P(A \text{ or } B) = P(A) + P(B) - P(A \text{ and } B)$$

Probability of Lottery or Lightning $= \frac{1}{10^6} + \frac{1}{10^6} - \frac{1}{10^{12}}$

> **GMAT Insider:** On probability questions, AND means multiply; OR means add (and subtract if necessary).

In this example, you must add the two probabilities but you must also subtract the probability of both events happening together. Why? The answer is not intuitive, but over the next few pages you will come to understand it conceptually.

Understanding the General Case Formula

To better understand it, let's first apply it to mutually exclusive events. If you are asking for the probability of one event OR another, and they are mutually exclusive, then you simply add the two probabilities because the value of P(A and B) on the right side of the equation will always be 0.

> **Facts & Formulas:** Understanding the general case formula for probability is perhaps the most important skill for GMAT probability questions:
>
> $$P(A \text{ or } B) = P(A) + P(B) - P(A \text{ and } B)$$

Examples with mutually exclusive events: *Imagine that two people have bought one ticket each in a lottery with only one prize. If there are a million tickets in the lottery, each person has 1 in a million chance of winning. If one person wins, the other person cannot win. What is the probability that one OR the other of them wins? This is an example of when you should add probabilities using the general case formula. The probability that one of the two people wins is thus 2 in a million.*

In this case: $P(A \text{ or } B) = \dfrac{1}{10^6} + \dfrac{1}{10^6} - 0 = \dfrac{2}{10^6}$

Consider several other examples of "OR" probability problems with mutually exclusive events:

1. What is the probability of getting a head or a tail on the flip of a coin?

2. What is the probability of getting a 2, 3, or 4 on one roll of a fair six sided die?

3. What is the probability of the Yankees or the Red Sox winning the World Series?

Visually, mutually exclusive events can be represented in the following manner when there is no overlap between the events:

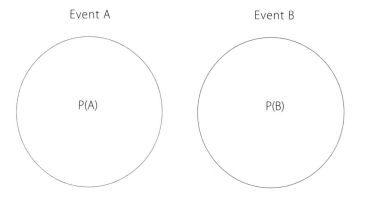

General Case Formula with Events that are not Mutually Exclusive

Many problems that you face on the GMAT will involve events that are not mutually exclusive. Consider the following problem:

Example: What is the probability that at least one of two people was born on a Monday?

Detailed Explanation

Many students are tempted to answer $\frac{2}{7}$, but that would only be true if the events were mutually exclusive. It is possible for both people to be born on a Monday so P(A and B) is not equal to 0. To make the point, imagine if the question asked about seven people rather than two people. If you simply added the probabilities, it would lead to an illogical conclusion: there would be a 100% probability that out of a group of seven people someone was born on a Monday. The problem with adding $\frac{1}{7}$ and $\frac{1}{7}$ is that you are double-counting the probability that both people were born on the same weekday. The correction we have to make is subtracting the probability that they are BOTH born on the same day. The probability that they are both born on a Monday is simply $P(A \text{ and } B) = (\frac{1}{7})(\frac{1}{7}) = \frac{1}{49}$. Plugging that into the general case you get the probability $= \frac{1}{7} + \frac{1}{7} - \frac{1}{49} = \frac{13}{49}$.

Visually two events that are not mutually exclusive can be drawn with a Venn diagram:

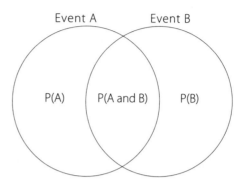

If the problem asks about three or more people, things quickly become more complicated. Simply adding the probabilities will double-count the probability that the first and second person were born on the same weekday, that the first and third person were born on the same weekday, as well as that the second and third person were born on the same day, and triple-count the probability that all three people were born on the same day.

To fix this most efficiently we must reverse the problem. The probability that the first person was not born on a Monday is $\frac{6}{7}$. The same probability obviously applies to the other two people. So the probability that none of the three were born on Monday is: $\frac{6}{7} \cdot \frac{6}{7} \cdot \frac{6}{7}$; hence the probability that at least one of the three was born on Monday is the exact opposite of this: $1 - \frac{6}{7} \cdot \frac{6}{7} \cdot \frac{6}{7}$

In problems such as this with multiple events that are not mutually exclusive events, it is always easier to find the complementary event and then subtract that probability from one.

Before we examine several GMAT problems that require this approach, consider a few other examples of general case problems with events that are not mutually exclusive.

More examples with events that are not mutually exlusive:

What is the probability of getting an A in Calculus or in English?

What is the probability of winning the Mega Millions or the Powerball?

What is the probability of being accepted to Harvard Business School or Wharton School of Business?

Common Probability Question Types

1. "At least one" questions

Now that you understand the general case formula and the confusing nature of overlapping probability in these questions, let's examine a few more of these very common question types and solidify the proper approach. Whenever you see questions that ask for the probability of "at least one", it is almost always easiest to find the probability of none which is the complementary event to at least one.

8.   There are 3 red balls and 2 black balls in an jar. What is the probability that John gets at least one red ball when he picks two balls at random out of the jar at the same time?

(A) $\frac{6}{25}$

(B) $\frac{19}{25}$

(C) $\frac{1}{10}$

(D) $\frac{9}{10}$

(E) $\frac{19}{20}$

> *GMAT Insider:* On probability questions with the language "At least one", find the complementary event and subtract it from 1 to get the probability for the event in question.
>
> **Note**
> Do not accidentally pick the probability for the complementary event – you must always remember to subtract from one if you are using this strategy. On "At least one" problems, answer choices usually come in pairs that add up to one and the complementary probability will often be an answer choice.

9.   In a bowl of marbles, 8 are yellow, 6 are blue, and 4 are black. If John picks 2 balls out of the bowl at random and at the same time, what is the probability that at least one of the marbles will be yellow?

(A) $\frac{5}{17}$

(B) $\frac{12}{17}$

(C) $\frac{25}{81}$

(D) $\frac{56}{81}$

(E) $\frac{4}{9}$

2. Pairs probability

Probability questions that require you to match pairs (a special kind of dependent probability) can be particularly confusing and require a particular approach. Consider this brainteaser question (requires no calculations on paper), which has been used during numerous investment banking and trading job interviews:

Example: *What is the probability that you get a pair when picking the top two cards off of a randomly shuffled deck of cards (52 cards with 13 sets of 4 matching cards)?*

Detailed Explanation

This question is asking for the probability to get ANY pair, not one specific pair (say a pair of 2s or 3s) Thinking about the problem one pick at a time (which is how you should always think about events at the same time), you realize that the first pick does not matter. In other words, the probability for a favorable outcome on the first card is $\frac{52}{52}$. After you pick a card, you must now match that card with the second pick. For whatever card you have chosen, there will be 3 favorable outcomes left in the deck out of 51 cards (remember you used one up in the first pick). Therefore the probability to get any pair picking the top 2 cards off the deck is $\frac{52}{52} \cdot \frac{3}{51} = \frac{3}{51}$.

10. In a $10 game of chance in Las Vegas, there are two identical bowls that contain 100 marbles. Each bowl contains 95 black marbles along with 5 different colored marbles: one blue, one yellow, one green, one red, and one gold. You get to pick one marble randomly from each bowl. If you get a matching pair of colored marbles (for example, blue and blue or gold and gold) you win $10,000. What is the probability that you win the prize in one play of the game?

(A) $\frac{1}{20}$

(B) $\frac{1}{40}$

(C) $\frac{1}{400}$

(D) $\frac{1}{2000}$

(E) $\frac{1}{10,000}$

This next question is a good example of "at least one" probability and pairs probability in one GMAT question. This is at the higher end of difficulty for what is possible on the test:

11. If 4 fair dice are thrown simultaneously, what is the probability of getting at least one pair?

(A) $\frac{1}{6}$

(B) $\frac{5}{18}$

(C) $\frac{1}{2}$

(D) $\frac{2}{3}$

(E) $\frac{13}{18}$

Binomial Probability (Heads/Tails Probability)

There are many problems on the GMAT that test your understanding of "binomial probability" – sequential probability where there are exactly the same two choices for each event. The most common binomial probability problems on the GMAT are those involving a flip of a coin. Very difficult binomial probability problems can be solved with a formula (presented at the end of the section), but almost all GMAT problems can be solved using your basic understanding of probability and counting that you have gained in this lesson. Consider a simple example.

Example: What is the probability of getting two heads in a row and then a tail on three flips of a coin?

Detailed Explanation

In a binomial probability problem with fair coin flips, the probability of either event is always the same ($\frac{1}{2}$), so the probability of any series of events will be the same. In other words, the probability of getting heads, tails, and heads is always the same as heads, heads, and heads on three flips of a coin. In a coin flip, the probability of any series of events must be ($\frac{1}{2}$)^n, where n represents the number of events (coin flips). So in this example, the answer is simply ($\frac{1}{2}$)^3=$\frac{1}{8}$.

How to Approach More Difficult Binomial Probability Problems

On many binomial problems, it is helpful to think of the problem from more of a counting perspective. Instead of thinking about multiplying the probabilities as shown on the previous page, think about favorable outcomes over total outcomes. In three flips of a coin (or any 3 binomial events), you know there are 8 outcomes because if you have 3 spots to fill with 2 choices for each, there must be 2 x 2 x 2 = 8 possible outcomes. On binomial probability problems with 3 or fewer events, it is always easy to write out the possible outcomes and answer any question about them. To illustrate this, let's write out the 8 possible outcomes that exist with three flips of a coin:

TTT   HHH
THT   HTH
TTH   HHT
THH   HTT

As you know, each one of these has the same probability and only one of them is favorable. Therefore in the previous example, that probability is $\frac{1}{8}$. With all of the outcomes written out, consider the following question:

Example: *What is the probability of getting exactly 2 heads and one tail (in any order) on three flips of a coin?*

Detailed Explanation

In this problem, the question is not specifying a particular order so the answer will not be $\frac{1}{8}$. You must consider all the ways to get exactly two heads and one tail. By looking at the list of 8 possible outcomes it is easy to see that 3 of the 8 involve 2 heads and one tail (THH, HTH, HHT), so the number of favorable outcomes over total outcomes $= \frac{3}{8}$.

As you will see shortly, this problem can also be thought of in a different way that does not involve writing out the outcomes. Each outcome has a probability of $\frac{1}{8}$, so if you can determine the number of outcomes that are favorable and multiply that times $\frac{1}{8}$, you can get the overall probability. We learned in the permutations with repeating elements section (it can also be thought of as a combination) how to determine the number of ways to arrange HHT (three things of which 2 are identical) which is $\frac{3!}{2!}=3$. Multiplying 3 times $\frac{1}{8}$ you get the overall probability of $\frac{3}{8}$.

> *How Your Mind Works:* If the number of events is small, it is probably easier to just write out the outcomes and handpick the favorable outcomes.

Probability Drill

1. What is the probability of getting at least 2 heads in a row on three flips of a fair coin?

2. What is the probability of getting at least 2 heads on three flips of a fair coin?

3. What is the probability of getting 2 threes in a row followed by a different number on 3 rolls of a fair six sided die?

4. What is the probability of getting exactly 2 sixes on three rolls of a fair six sided die?

Binomial Probability with Many Events – If Time Allows

When the number of events is greater than three, it becomes impractical to write out the number of outcomes. While these types of questions are uncommon and only faced by students facing the upper bin questions, they do appear on the GMAT. Consider the following example.

Example: What is the probability of getting exactly 3 heads on 5 flips of a fair coin?

Detailed Explanation

There are 32 possible outcomes in any binomial problem with 5 events ($2 \times 2 \times 2 \times 2 \times 2$). It is not possible to write out that many outcomes in a reasonable amount of time so you must use your understanding of counting to solve. What you know is that each outcome has the same probability, so you must only calculate the number of outcomes that contain exactly 3 heads and 2 tails and put that over 32 for the overall probability (favorable outcomes over total outcomes). Going back to your knowledge of counting, the question is really asking for the number of unique ways to write out HHHTT. This can be done with your formula for permutations with repeating elements. In this case N = 5 and there are two things repeating, one of them 2 times and the other 3 times. Therefore of the 32 outcomes, $\frac{5!}{3!2!}$ or 10 will contain exactly 3 heads and the probability is $\frac{10}{32} = \frac{5}{16}$.

Let's finish the probability section with several difficult binomial probability questions, variations of which have been on the GMAT:

12.   If the probability of rain on any given day is 50%, what is the probability that it will rain on 3 days in a row during a 5 day period?

(A) $\dfrac{3}{32}$

(B) $\dfrac{1}{4}$

(C) $\dfrac{9}{32}$

(D) $\dfrac{5}{16}$

(E) $\dfrac{1}{2}$

13.   There are 100 balls in an jar. 40 of the balls are black and 60 are white. What is the probability of getting at least one black ball in 3 consecutive picks, with replacement of the ball each time?

(A)   .216

(B)   .316

(C)   .500

(D)   .684

(E)   .784

Probability Summary

1. Concepts and Formulas

Probability describes the likelihood of a certain event; all probability values fall between 0% and 100%, or between 0 and 1, inclusive: $0 \le P(A) \le 1$.

Probability of a single event: $P(A) = \dfrac{\text{\# of outcomes when A occurs}}{\text{total \# of possible outcomes}}$

Mutually exclusive events – events that can never occur together, i.e. occurrence of one event completely eliminates the probability of occurrence of the other.

Examples:
(1)   Getting an A , a B, or a C as the final grade on one class.
(2)   Answering 17 questions right or answering 21 questions right on a particular exam.

Note that the mutually exclusive events do not necessarily cover the entire scope of possible outcomes. For instance, it is also possible to get a D or an F as the final grade in the class in example 1, as well as it is possible to answer 19, 20, 25, etc. questions on a particular exam in example 2. Since the selected mutually exclusive events do not have to cover all possible outcomes, their probabilities do not have to add up to 1 – they are less than or equal to 1.

Important properties:

(1)   Mutually exclusive events never occur together: P(A and B) = 0
(2)   If A and B are mutually exclusive then P(A or B) = P(A) + P(B)

Two events are **complementary** if one and only one of them must occur. All complementary events are mutually exclusive (because only one of them can occur) but not all mutually exclusive events are complementary.

Examples:

(1)   Failing vs. passing a certain course (contrast with getting a particular grade)

(2)   Answering at least half of the questions on the exam vs. answering less than half the questions on the exam (contrast with answering a particular number of questions in the example of mutually exclusive events).

Important Properties:

(1)   Complementary events never occur together: $P(A \text{ and } B) = 0$

(2)   Because one of the complementary events must occur, their probabilities sum up to 1: $P(A \text{ or } B) = 1$; $P(A) = 1 - P(B)$; $P(B) = 1 - P(A)$.

Events A and B are <u>dependent</u> if the occurrence of one event affects the probability of another.

Examples:

(1)   Drawing balls without replacement.

(2)   Allocating a limited number of prizes among the audience (each subsequent allocation of a prize reduces the probability of the remaining participants winning).

$P(A \text{ and } B) = P(A) \cdot P_A(B)$

Where $P(A \text{ and } B)$ is the probability that both events will occur;

$P(A)$ is the probability of event A;

$P_A(B)$ is the probability that event B will occur assuming that A has already occurred;

$P_A(B)$ is called conditional probability.

Events A and B are <u>independent</u> if the occurrence of one event does not affect the probability of the occurrence of another. In case of sequential events, the initial situation is restored before each subsequent experiment.

Examples:

(1)   Throwing dice

(2)   Tossing a coin

(3)   Selecting balls from an jar with replacement

Important Properties:

$P(A \text{ and } B) = P(A) \cdot P(B)$

OR formulas (Probability of A or B):

(1)	General case: P(A or B) = P(A) + P(B) − P(A and B)

(2)	Mutually exclusive events: P(A or B) = P(A) + P(B)

(3)	Complementary events: P(A or B) = 1

AND formulas (Probability of A and B):

(1)	Mutually exclusive and complementary events: P(A and B) = 0

(2)	Dependent events: P(A and B) = P(A) • P_A(B)

(3)	Independent events: P(A and B) = P(A) • P(B)

2. Common question types and strategies

- **"At least one" questions**
  - Identify the complementary event and find the probability for that event.
  - Subtract the probability of that complementary event from 1 to find the probability of the desired event.
  - Do not forget to distinguish between dependent and independent events in these problems.

- **Pairs probability**
  - Pairs probability questions are simply a tricky type of dependent probability questions.
  - The first pick may not matter (pair of cards example or pairs in rolling dice) or it may have a fixed probability.
  - The second pick must exactly match the first so the probability will always be lower for that event (or could be the same).
  - Language is very important. Note the difference between asking for the probability of picking ANY PAIR vs. PAIR OF TWOS

- **Binomial probability**
  - Very common type of probability question on the GMAT that involves successive events with only two possible outcomes.
  - For a small number of events (3 or fewer) always write out the outcomes and answer the question by handpicking the favorable outcomes.
  - On questions with a large number of events, use your understanding of probability and counting to answer the question.

3. Other Strategies and tips

- To compute the probability of a single event, it is sufficient to know the proportion of the outcomes when this event occurs among the total number of outcomes. It is not necessary to know the exact number of occurrences. Taking advantages of ratios is particularly common in Data Sufficiency.

- When finding the combined probability of several mutually exclusive events, simply add the number of outcomes of each event and divide by the total number of possible outcomes.

- When asked about the probability of an outcome that guarantees a certain result, always consider the worst-case scenario as a check.

- If guessing on a problem involving complementary events, look for pairs of answer choices that add up to one. Guess from that pool of answers (often there are two sets that add to one) and pick the one that is most logical.

Counting Drill (Self-Study)

The following are some important types of restriction problems, some of which were not discussed in the lesson portion:

Permutations with couples or groups that must sit together

1. A group of 8 students take up a full row at a movie theater. There are 2 couples and the 2 people within each couple must sit together. In how many different arrangements can the students sit?

2. How many ways can 3 groups of three people be seated in 9 seats, if the groups must sit together?

Permutations with couples or groups that cannot be chosen together

3. Jill bought 6 glasses for her kitchen – white, red, black, grey, yellow, and blue – and would like to display 3 of them on the shelf next to each other. If she decides that a red and a blue glass cannot be displayed at the same time, in how many different ways can Jill arrange the glasses?

Permutations with alternating seating

4. In how many ways can 3 men and 3 women be seated in 6 seats if they must alternate?

Combination with several groups

5. From a group of 10 boys and 7 girls, how many different hockey teams of 6 players can be formed if the team must consist of 3 girls and 3 boys?

Detailed Explanations

1. Whenever you are dealing with arrangements involving couples or groups that must sit together, use one strategy: treat each couple or group as one unit and then deal with the ways to arrange the people within the couple or the group at the end. In this example, there are eight people. In that group there are two couples so think of the group as 4 individuals and 2 couples that we will treat as individual "units". That gives us 6 "units" that we have to arrange so N = 6 and there are 6! ways to arrange those 6 units. 6! is not the answer, though, because the couples can each be switched 2! ways. Therefore the total number of arrangements = 6! · 2! · 2! = 720 · 2 · 2 = 2880.

2. In this example, you are dealing with 3 groups of 3 instead of individuals and couples. Using the same strategy, treat each group of 3 as one unit. You are therefore arranging 3 units and that can be done in 3! ways. Now, however, you must consider all the ways to arrange the individuals within each group. As each group contains three people, there are 3! ways to arrange the individuals within each group. NOTE: The people can be arranged 3! ways (which is 6) not 3 ways which is a common mistake on this type of problem. As a result the final calculation is 3! (number of ways to arrange the 3 groups) · 3! · 3! · 3! (each one of those 3! represents the number of ways to arrange the people in each of the groups). 3! = 6 so this is really 6 · 6 · 6 · 6 = 36² = 1296 ways.

3. In this kind of restriction problem, first find the total number of permutations without the constraint. Then find the number of combinations for which the constraint would be violated and multiply that by K!, the ways in which to arrange those colors. Then subtract that product from the total number of permutations without the constraint. Here, the total number of permutations, unconstrained, would be $\frac{6!}{(6-3)!} = 120$. To find where the constraint would be violated, you need to assume that that the red and blue glass would be on the shelf, leaving 4 glasses remaining for one space. The formula for that would be the combinations formula: $\frac{4!}{1!(4-1)!} = 4$. Therefore, we have to multiply that 4 by the number of permutations of the 3 items that will be displayed on the shelf for each combination of 3 constraint violating colors, which is simply 3!. 4 · 3! = 24, which we subtract from 120 to get 96. Thus, there are 4 groups of colors possible which violate the constraint by including both red and blue (Red, Blue, Yellow vs. Red, Blue, White, etc.). At this point, we've only calculated the number of color groupings, but have not yet considered the number of ways in which we can arrange each of these constraint-violating groups.

4. With alternating seating, use your understanding of basic counting to solve. Consider the 6 spots – three of which are designated for men and three for women: M W M W M W. You have the following choices for each of the spots: 3 3 2 2 1 1. Mulitplying them together you get 36 ways. (Note this could be shortcutted by just thinking 3! for the men x 3! for the women = 36). 36, however, is not the answer because you must remember that the starting order could be switched from men to women. Therefore, the result must be multiplied by 2! to account for those possibilities. Total number of ways = 72.

5. While we did one in the lesson portion, this type of combination is very common. First determine the number of groups of boys that can be created $= \dfrac{10!}{3!7!} = \dfrac{10 \cdot 9 \cdot 8}{3 \cdot 2} = 120$. The number of groups of girls that can be created $= \dfrac{6!}{3!3!} = 20$. Therefore, the total number of 6 person teams that can be created from those groups = 120 x 20 = 2,400 teams.

Assorted Problems

14. Number N is randomly selected from a set of all primes between 10 and 40, inclusive. Number K is selected from a set of all multiples of 5 between 10 and 40, inclusive. What is the probability that N + K is odd?

(A) $\frac{1}{2}$

(B) $\frac{2}{3}$

(C) $\frac{3}{4}$

(D) $\frac{4}{7}$

(E) $\frac{5}{8}$

15.   Mark's clothing store uses a bar-code system to identify every item. Each item is
        marked by a combination of 2 letters followed by 3 digits. Additionally, the three-
        digit number must be even for male products and odd for female products. If all
        apparel products start with the letter combination AP, how many male apparel
        items can be identified with the bar code?

(A)   100

(B)   405

(C)   500

(D)   729

(E)   1000

16. Fernando purchased a university meal plan that allows him to have a total of 3 lunches and 3 dinners per week. If the cafeteria is closed on weekends and Fernando always goes home for a dinner on Friday nights, how many options does he have to allocate his meals?

(A)   20

(B)   24

(C)   40

(D)   100

(E)   120

17.   In a business school case competition, the top three teams receive cash prizes of $5,000, $3,000 and $2,000, respectively, while the remaining teams are not ranked and do not receive any prizes. If there are 6 participating teams, how many outcomes of the competition are possible?

(A)   18

(B)   20

(C)   36

(D)   60

(E)   120

The same question, but easier:

18.   In a business school case competition, the top three teams receive cash prizes of $5,000, $3,000 and $2,000, respectively. If there are only three teams remaining in the final round, how many outcomes of the competition are possible?

(A)   1

(B)   6

(C)   9

(D)   18

(E)   36

A difficult variation:

19.   In a business school case competition, the top three teams receive cash prizes
        of $5,000, $3,000 and $2,000, respectively, while the remaining teams are not
        ranked and do not receive any prizes. There are 6 participating teams, named
        Team A, Team B, Team C, Team D, Team E, and Team F. If Team A wins one of the
        prizes, Team B will also win one of the prizes. How many outcomes of the
        competition are possible?

(A)   18

(B)   20

(C)   54

(D)   84

(E)   120

> *Think Like the Test Maker:* To increase
> difficulty, the testmakers can turn a
> simple permutations problem into a
> complex permutations problem, or
> can add extra restrictions. However, no
> matter the question's difficulty level, it
> will always rely on the same principles
> you have already learned.

> *Lazy Genius:* Sometimes, Permuta-
> tions-with-Restrictions questions can
> be answered by finding the number of
> permutations that would exist without
> the restrictions – which is almost
> always one of the answer choices in
> itself (usually D or E) – and assessing
> the relative impact of the restrictions.
> The remaining answer choices will
> typically vary enough that an estimate
> will often suffice.

20. Jennifer owns 4 shirts of the same design, 2 of which are white, 1 black and 1 red. If all 4 shirts are put on top of each other in a drawer, how many different color arrangements can Jennifer create?

(A)   4

(B)   6

(C)   12

(D)   24

(E)   60

21.   How many two-element subsets of {1, 2, 3, 4} are there that do not contain the pair of elements 2 and 4 ?

(A)   One

(B)   Two

(C)   Four

(D)   Five

(E)   Six

22.   A company that ships boxes to a total of 12 distribution centers uses color coding to identify each center. If either a single color or a pair of two different colors is chosen to represent each center and if each center is uniquely represented by that choice of one or two colors, what is the minimum number of colors needed for the coding? (Assume that the order of the colors in a pair does not matter.)

(A)   4

(B)   5

(C)   6

(D)   12

(E)   24

23.   A key ring has 7 keys. How many different ways can they be arranged?

(A)   6

(B)   7

(C)   5!

(D)   6!

(E)   7!

24. If x is chosen randomly from the set {7, 8, 9, 10, 11} and y is chosen randomly from the set {20, 21, 22, 23}, what is the probability that both x and y are prime numbers?

(A) $\frac{1}{5}$

(B) $\frac{3}{20}$

(C) $\frac{13}{20}$

(D) $\frac{3}{10}$

(E) $\frac{1}{10}$

The same question, but more difficult:

25.   *x*, *y*, and *z* are all unique numbers. If *x* is chosen randomly from the set
        {7, 8, 9, 10, 11} and *y* and *z* are chosen randomly from the set {20, 21, 22, 23},
        what is the probability that *x* and *y* are prime numbers and *z* is not?

(A) $\frac{1}{5}$

(B) $\frac{3}{20}$

(C) $\frac{13}{20}$

(D) $\frac{3}{10}$

(E) $\frac{1}{10}$

Think Like the Test Maker: To make probability questions more difficult, the GMAT sometimes incorporates a dependent probability element into a mostly independent probability question. Occasionally, as here, the testmakers will try to trick you into thinking that a dependent event is actually independent.

26.   How many three-element subsets of {1, 2, 3, 4, 5, 6, 7, 8, 9, 10, 11, 12, 13, 14, 15} are there that contain only even numbers?

(A) $\dfrac{7!}{3!4!}$

(B) $\dfrac{7!}{4!}$

(C) $\dfrac{7!}{3!}$

(D) $7!$

(E) 7^3

27.   A car comes with 7 different possible exterior colors and 6 different interior colors. How many different color combinations are there?

(A)   26

(B)   42

(C) $\dfrac{7!6!}{2!}$

(D) $7!6!$

(E) $\dfrac{13!}{2!}$

28.   A license plate consists of a combination of 6 digits or letters. All numbers (0-9) and all 26 letters may be used. How many unique license plates are there?

(A) 36^6

(B) $\dfrac{36!}{30!6!}$

(C) $\dfrac{36!}{30!}$

(D) $\dfrac{36!}{6}!$

(E)   30!

29.   A flush in poker is defined as all 5 cards being of the same suit. There are four
        suits: spades, diamonds, clubs, and hearts – all of which there are 13 of in a
        standard deck of 52 cards. How many ways are there to draw a flush?

(A)   4

(B)   676

(C)   1,287

(D)   5,148

(E)   154,440

30.   How many different ways can you seat 10 men and 10 women around a circular table if you need to alternate the men and women?

(A)   100

(B) $9! \cdot 9!$

(C) $\dfrac{20!}{10!}$

(D) $9! \cdot 10!$

(E) $10! \cdot 10!$

31.   In how many arrangements can a teacher seat 3 girls and 3 boys in a row of 6
       seats if the boys are to have the first, third, and fifth seats?

(A)   6

(B)   9

(C)   12

(D)   36

(E)   720

32. If x is to be chosen at random from the set $\{1, 2, 3, 4\}$ and y is to be chosen at random from the set $\{5, 6, 7\}$, what is the probability that xy will be even?

(A) $\frac{1}{6}$

(B) $\frac{1}{3}$

(C) $\frac{1}{2}$

(D) $\frac{2}{3}$

(E) $\frac{5}{6}$

A = {2, 3, 4, 5}
B = {4, 5, 6, 7, 8}

33.   Two integers will be randomly selected from the sets above, one integer from set
        A and one integer from set B. What is the probability that the sum of the two
        integers will equal 9?

(A)   0.15

(B)   0.20

(C)   0.25

(D)   0.30

(E)   0.33

34.   In how many different ways can a soccer team finish the season with 3 wins, 2 losses and 1 draw?

(A)   6

(B)   20

(C)   60

(D)   120

(E)   240

35.   If a randomly selected non-negative single-digit integer is added to set
        X {2, 3, 7, 8}, what is the probability that the median of the set will increase
        while its range will remain the same?

(A)   20%

(B)   30%

(C)   40%

(D)   50%

(E)   60%

36. If the President and Vice President must sit next to each other in a row with 4 other members of the Board, how many different seating arrangements are possible?

(A) 120

(B) 240

(C) 300

(D) 360

(E) 720

37.   What is the number of three-digit multiples of 5 that are not divisible by 10?

(A)   90

(B)   100

(C)   180

(D)   200

(E)   1000

38. Jeremy needs to choose 3 flowers for his mother from a group of 10 roses, 6 of which are red and 4 of which are white. What is the ratio of the number of choices Jeremy has to select only red roses to the number of choices he has to select only white roses?

(A)   30:1

(B)   10:1

(C)   5:1

(D)   3:2

(E)   1:5

Combinatorics Problem Set

39.   Tanya is taking a final examination that contains 5 essay questions, of which she
      must answer 3. How many different final exams could Tanya potentially create?

(A)   10

(B)   15

(C)   20

(D)   60

(E)   120

40.   Assuming that there are no ties, how many different outcomes are possible in a race with 5 athletes?

(A)   25

(B)   120

(C)   240

(D)   360

(E)   720

41.   Melissa has 6 favorite books. If she plans to take 3 books on her transatlantic flight, how many choices does she have to make her selection?

(A)   6

(B)   18

(C)   20

(D)   24

(E)   120

42.   At a certain laboratory, chemical substances are identified by an unordered combination of 3 colors. If no chemical may be assigned the same 3 colors, what is the maximum number of substances that can be identified using 7 colors?

(A)   21

(B)   35

(C)   105

(D)   135

(E)   210

43.   An equity analyst needs to select 3 stocks for the upcoming year and rank these securities in terms of their investment potential. If the analyst has narrowed down the list of potential stocks to 7, in how many ways can she choose and rank her top 3 picks?

(A)   21

(B)   35

(C)   210

(D)   420

(E)   840

44. How many different five-letter combinations can be created from the word TWIST?

(A) 5

(B) 24

(C) 60

(D) 120

(E) 720

45.   If an employee ID code must consist of 3 non-repeating digits and each digit in
        the code must be a prime number, how many ID codes can be created?

(A)   12

(B)   24

(C)   60

(D)   120

(E)   240

46. A university cafeteria offers 4 flavors of pizza – pepperoni, chicken, Hawaiian and vegetarian. If a customer has an option (but not the obligation) to add extra cheese, mushrooms, or both to any kind of pizza, how many different pizza varieties are available?

(A)   4

(B)   8

(C)   12

(D)   16

(E)   32

47.   A book store has received 8 different books, of which $\frac{3}{8}$ are novels, 25% are study guides and the remaining are textbooks. If all books must be placed on one shelf displaying new items and if books in the same category have to be shelved next to each other, how many different arrangements of books are possible?

(A)   18

(B)   36

(C)   72

(D)   216

(E)   432

48. A group of 5 students bought movie tickets in one row next to each other. If Bob and Lisa are in this group, what is the probability that both of them will sit next to only one other student from the group?

(A)   5%

(B)   10%

(C)   15%

(D)   20%

(E)   25%

Probability Problem Set

49.   According to a recent student poll, $\frac{5}{7}$ of the 21 members of the finance club are interested in a career in investment banking. If two students are chosen at random, what is the probability that at least one of them is interested in investment banking?

(A) $\frac{1}{14}$

(B) $\frac{4}{49}$

(C) $\frac{2}{7}$

(D) $\frac{45}{49}$

(E) $\frac{13}{14}$

50. Operation "#" is defined as adding a randomly selected two-digit multiple of 6 to a randomly selected two-digit prime number and reducing the result by half. If operation "#" is repeated 10 times, what is the probability that it will yield at least 2 integers?

(A) 0%

(B) 10%

(C) 20%

(D) 30%

(E) 40%

51.   Number N is randomly selected from a set of consecutive integers between 50
        and 69, inclusive. What is the probability that N will have the same number of
        factors as 89?

(A)   10%

(B)   13%

(C)   17%

(D)   20%

(E)   25%

52.   Each year three space shuttles are launched, two in June and one in October. If each shuttle launch is known to occur without a delay in 90% of the cases and if the current month is January, what is the probability that at least one of the launches in the next 16 months will be delayed?

(A) $\frac{1}{27}$

(B) $\frac{3}{27}$

(C) $\frac{271}{1000}$

(D) $\frac{729}{1000}$

(E) $\frac{26}{27}$

53.   Crowan throws 3 dice and records the product of the numbers appearing at the top of each die as the result of the attempt. What is the probability that the result of any attempt is an odd integer divisible by 25?

(A) $\frac{7}{216}$

(B) $\frac{5}{91}$

(C) $\frac{13}{88}$

(D) $\frac{1}{5}$

(E) $\frac{3}{8}$

54.   A telephone number contains 10 digits, including a 3-digit area code. Bob remembers the area code and the next 5 digits of the number. He also remembers that the remaining digits are not 0, 1, 2, 5, or 7. If Bob tries to find the number by guessing the remaining digits at random, the probability that he will be able to find the correct number in at most 2 attempts is closest to which of the following?

(A) $\dfrac{1}{625}$

(B) $\dfrac{2}{625}$

(C) $\dfrac{4}{625}$

(D) $\dfrac{25}{625}$

(E) $\dfrac{50}{625}$

55.   If number N is randomly drawn from a set of all non-negative single-digit

integers, what is the probability that $\frac{5N^3}{8}$ is an integer?

(A)   20%

(B)   30%

(C)   40%

(D)   50%

(E)   60%

56. The acceptance rate at a certain business school is 15% for first-time applicants and 20% for all re-applicants. If David is applying for admission for the first time this year, what is the probability that he will have to apply no more than twice before he is accepted?

(A) 20%

(B) 30%

(C) 32%

(D) 35%

(E) 40%

57.   If a randomly selected positive single-digit multiple of 3 is multiplied by a
       randomly selected prime number less than 20, what is the probability that this
       product will be a multiple of 45?

(A) $\frac{1}{32}$

(B) $\frac{1}{28}$

(C) $\frac{1}{24}$

(D) $\frac{2}{32}$

(E) $\frac{2}{28}$

Data Sufficiency Problem Set

58. What is the probability of selecting a white ball from an jar?

(1) There are twice as many white balls as there are balls of any other color

(2) There are 30 more white balls as balls of all other colors combined

(A) Statement (1) alone is sufficient, but statement (2) alone is not sufficient.

(B) Statement (2) alone is sufficient, but statement (1) alone is not sufficient.

(C) BOTH statements TOGETHER are sufficient, but NEITHER statement ALONE is sufficient.

(D) Each statement ALONE is sufficient.

(E) Statements (1) and (2) TOGETHER are NOT sufficient.

59. At a business school conference with 100 attendees, are there any students of the same age (rounded to the nearest year) who attend the same school?

   (1)   The range of ages of the participants is 22 to 30, inclusive

   (2)   Participants represent 10 business schools

(A)   Statement (1) alone is sufficient, but statement (2) alone is not sufficient.

(B)   Statement (2) alone is sufficient, but statement (1) alone is not sufficient.

(C)   BOTH statements TOGETHER are sufficient, but NEITHER statement ALONE is sufficient.

(D)   Each statement ALONE is sufficient.

(E)   Statements (1) and (2) TOGETHER are NOT sufficient.

60.   Jonathan would like to visit one of the 12 gyms in his area. If he selects a gym
       at random, what it the probability that the gym will have both a swimming pool
       and a squash court?

       (1)   All but 2 gyms in the area have a squash court

       (2)   Each of the 9 gyms with a pool has a squash court

(A)   Statement (1) alone is sufficient, but statement (2) alone is not sufficient.

(B)   Statement (2) alone is sufficient, but statement (1) alone is not sufficient.

(C)   BOTH statements TOGETHER are sufficient, but NEITHER statement ALONE is

       sufficient.

(D)   Each statement ALONE is sufficient.

(E)   Statements (1) and (2) TOGETHER are NOT sufficient.

61.   How many ways does a coach have to select a university team from a pool of
        eligible candidates?

        (1)   The number of eligible candidates is 3 times greater than then
                number of slots on the team

        (2)   60% of the 20 athletes are eligible to play on the 4-person university
                team

(A)   Statement (1) alone is sufficient, but statement (2) alone is not sufficient.

(B)   Statement (2) alone is sufficient, but statement (1) alone is not sufficient.

(C)   BOTH statements TOGETHER are sufficient, but NEITHER statement ALONE is

        sufficient.

(D)   Each statement ALONE is sufficient.

(E)   Statements (1) and (2) TOGETHER are NOT sufficient.

> *GMAT Insider:* While ratios are often
> sufficient to compute probabilities,
> they are usually insufficient to find the
> number of permutations or combina-
> tions that can be created.

62.   What is the median of set A {-8, 15, -9, 4, N)?

(1)   Number N is a prime and N^6 is even

(2)   2N + 14 < 20

(A)   Statement (1) alone is sufficient, but statement (2) alone is not sufficient.

(B)   Statement (2) alone is sufficient, but statement (1) alone is not sufficient.

(C)   BOTH statements TOGETHER are sufficient, but NEITHER statement ALONE is sufficient.

(D)   Each statement ALONE is sufficient.

(E)   Statements (1) and (2) TOGETHER are NOT sufficient.

63.   There were initially no black marbles in a jar. Subsequently, new marbles were added to the jar. If marbles are drawn at random and the selected marbles are not returned to the jar, what is the probability of selecting 2 black marbles in a row?

    (1)   After the new marbles are added, 50% of all marbles are black

    (2)   Among the 10 added marbles, 8 are black

(A)   Statement (1) alone is sufficient, but statement (2) alone is not sufficient.

(B)   Statement (2) alone is sufficient, but statement (1) alone is not sufficient.

(C)   BOTH statements TOGETHER are sufficient, but NEITHER statement ALONE is sufficient.

(D)   Each statement ALONE is sufficient.

(E)   Statements (1) and (2) TOGETHER are NOT sufficient.

GMAT Insider: While the ratios are usually sufficient to find simple probabilities, they are normally insufficient to compute conditional probabilities.

64.   In how many ways can N students be seated in a row with N seats?

(1) $|N - 6| = 3$

(2) $N^2 = 7N + 18$

(A)   Statement (1) alone is sufficient, but statement (2) alone is not sufficient.

(B)   Statement (2) alone is sufficient, but statement (1) alone is not sufficient.

(C)   BOTH statements TOGETHER are sufficient, but NEITHER statement ALONE is
        sufficient.

(D)   Each statement ALONE is sufficient.

(E)   Statements (1) and (2) TOGETHER are NOT sufficient.

65.   What is the probability that it will rain on each of the next 3 days if the probability of rain on any single day is the same in that period?

(1)   The probability of no rain throughout the first two days is 36%

(2)   The probability of rain on the third day is 40%

(A)   Statement (1) alone is sufficient, but statement (2) alone is not sufficient.

(B)   Statement (2) alone is sufficient, but statement (1) alone is not sufficient.

(C)   BOTH statements TOGETHER are sufficient, but NEITHER statement ALONE is sufficient.

(D)   Each statement ALONE is sufficient.

(E)   Statements (1) and (2) TOGETHER are NOT sufficient.

66. Set X consists of different positive numbers arranged in ascending order: K, L, M, 5, 7. If K, L, and M are consecutive integers, what is the arithmetic mean of set X?

(1) The product $K \cdot L \cdot M$ is a multiple of 6

(2) There are at least 2 prime numbers among K, L and M

(A) Statement (1) alone is sufficient, but statement (2) alone is not sufficient.

(B) Statement (2) alone is sufficient, but statement (1) alone is not sufficient.

(C) BOTH statements TOGETHER are sufficient, but NEITHER statement ALONE is sufficient.

(D) Each statement ALONE is sufficient.

(E) Statements (1) and (2) TOGETHER are NOT sufficient.

Facts & Formulas: The product of any 3 consecutive positive integers is always a multiple of 2, 3 and 6.

67.   If a number is drawn at random from the first 1,000 positive integers, what is the probability of selecting a **refined** number?

        (1)   Any *refined* number must be divisible by 22

        (2)   A *refined* number is any even multiple of 11

(A)   Statement (1) alone is sufficient, but statement (2) alone is not sufficient.

(B)   Statement (2) alone is sufficient, but statement (1) alone is not sufficient.

(C)   BOTH statements TOGETHER are sufficient, but NEITHER statement ALONE is

        sufficient.

(D)   Each statement ALONE is sufficient.

(E)   Statements (1) and (2) TOGETHER are NOT sufficient.

Challenge Problems

68. If two elements are dropped from set X {-10, -8, 0, 6, 7}, what will be the percentage change in its mean?

    (1)   The median of the set will remain the same

    (2)   The range of the set will decrease by 3

(A)   Statement (1) alone is sufficient, but statement (2) alone is not sufficient.

(B)   Statement (2) alone is sufficient, but statement (1) alone is not sufficient.

(C)   BOTH statements TOGETHER are sufficient, but NEITHER statement ALONE is sufficient.

(D)   Each statement ALONE is sufficient.

(E)   Statements (1) and (2) TOGETHER are NOT sufficient.

Combinatorics & Probability

69.   To apply for the position of photographer at a local magazine, Veronica needs to include 3 or 4 of her pictures in an envelope accompanying her application. If she has pre-selected 5 photos representative of her work, how many choices does she have to provide the photos for the magazine?

(A)   5

(B)   10

(C)   12

(D)   15

(E)   50

70. Members of a student parliament took a vote on a proposition for a new social event on Fridays. If all the members of the parliament voted either for or against the proposition and if the proposition was accepted in a 5-to-2 vote, in how many ways could the members vote?

(A)   7

(B)   10

(C)   14

(D)   21

(E)   42

71.   A retail company needs to set up 5 additional distribution centers that can be located in three cities on the east coast (Boston, New York, and Washington, D.C.), one city in the mid-west (Chicago), and three cities on the west coast (Seattle, San Francisco and Los Angeles). If the company must have 2 distribution centers on each coast and 1 in the mid-west, and only one center can be added in each city, in how many ways can the management allocate the distribution centers?

(A)   3

(B)   9

(C)   18

(D)   20

(E)   36

72. Three couples need to be arranged in a row for a group photo. If the couples cannot be separated, how many different arrangements are possible?

(A)   6

(B)   12

(C)   24

(D)   48

(E)   96

73.   If 6 fair coins are tossed, how many different coin sequences will have exactly 3
       tails, if all tails have to occur in a row?

(A)   4

(B)   8

(C)   16

(D)   20

(E)   24

74.   If every member of set X {-14, -12, 17, 28, 41, Z} is multiplied by number N, by what percent will the mean M of the set increase?

(1) $Z = 60$

(2) $N = \dfrac{Z}{M}$

(A)   Statement (1) alone is sufficient, but statement (2) alone is not sufficient.

(B)   Statement (2) alone is sufficient, but statement (1) alone is not sufficient.

(C)   BOTH statements TOGETHER are sufficient, but NEITHER statement ALONE is sufficient.

(D)   Each statement ALONE is sufficient.

(E)   Statements (1) and (2) TOGETHER are NOT sufficient.

75.   The flag of country Perralia has to contain three stripes of the same width, all of
       which must be positioned either vertically or horizontally. If the flag of Perralia
       must consist of the national colors, which include green, red, yellow, black and
       blue, how many different flags can be created?

(A)   24

(B)   48

(C)   60

(D)   120

(E)   240

76. A telephone company needs to create a set of 3-digit area codes. The company is entitled to use only digits 2, 4 and 5, which can be repeated. If the product of the digits in the area code must be even, how many different codes can be created?

(A)   8

(B)   9

(C)   18

(D)   26

(E)   27

77.   A group of candidates for 2 analyst positions consists of 6 people. If $\frac{1}{3}$ of the candidates are disqualified and 3 new candidates are recruited to replace them, the number of ways in which the 2 job offers can be allocated will:

(A)   Drop by 40%

(B)   Remain unchanged

(C)   Increase by 20%

(D)   Increase by 40%

(E)   Increase by 60%

78. Which of the following could be the range of a set consisting of odd multiples of 7?

(A)   21

(B)   24

(C)   35

(D)   62

(E)   70

79.   Jake, Lena, Fred, John and Inna need to drive home from a corporate reception
        in an SUV that can seat 7 people. If only Inna or Jake can drive, how many seat
        allocations are possible?

(A)   30

(B)   42

(C)   120

(D)   360

(E)   720

80. What is the probability of selecting a clean number from a set of integers containing all multiples of 3 between 1 and 99, inclusive?

(1) A clean number is an integer divisible only by 2 factors, one of which is greater than 2.

(2) A clean number must be odd.

(A) Statement (1) alone is sufficient, but statement (2) alone is not sufficient.

(B) Statement (2) alone is sufficient, but statement (1) alone is not sufficient.

(C) BOTH statements TOGETHER are sufficient, but NEITHER statement ALONE is sufficient.

(D) Each statement ALONE is sufficient.

(E) Statements (1) and (2) TOGETHER are NOT sufficient.

81.   In how many ways can a teacher write an answer key for a mini-quiz that contains 3 true-false questions followed by 2 multiple-choice questions with 4 answer choices each, if the correct answers to all true-false questions cannot be the same?

(A)   62

(B)   64

(C)   96

(D)   126

(E)   128

82.   A student committee on academic integrity has 90 ways to select a president and vice-president from a group of candidates. The same person cannot be both president and vice-president. How many students are in the group?

(A)   7

(B)   8

(C)   9

(D)   10

(E)   11

Solutions

Lesson Solutions Combinatorics

1. (D)

For question number one simply consider the three spots in which to arrange the 8 movies. You have 8 choices for the first movie, 7 for the second, and 6 for the third.

Total $= 8 \cdot 7 \cdot 6 = 336$

2. (D)

In the second question, you are being asked to determine two different counts and give the ratio between them. For the number of 5 character codes consider the 5 spots and the choices for each one: $10 \cdot 9 \cdot 8 \cdot 7 \cdot 6 = $ # of 5 character codes. For the number of 4 character codes consider the four spots and the choices for each one:

$10 \cdot 9 \cdot 8 \cdot 7 = $ # of 4 character codes. Ratio of 5 character codes to 4 character codes is

therefore: $\dfrac{10 \cdot 9 \cdot 8 \cdot 7 \cdot 6}{10 \cdot 9 \cdot 8 \cdot 7} = \dfrac{6}{1} = 6{:}1$

3. (B)

In this problem you have a total of 6 letters to arrange of which several repeat.

Using the formula $\dfrac{N!}{A!B!...}$ you see that $N = 6$ and there are two elements that repeat so there will be two separate factorials in the denominator. The P repeats 3 times and the E 2 times so the formula will look like this: $\dfrac{6!}{3!2!} = \dfrac{6 \cdot 5 \cdot 4}{2} = 60$ ways to arrange the letters.

4. (D)

This problem is more conceptual in nature and is generally more difficult for students. To solve, you must first determine how many total items you are arranging. As there are 4 identical copies of 5 different magazines, the total must be 20 magazines and N = 20. Now, you must determine how many items repeat to determine how many separate factorials you will need in the denominator. There are 5 different books and each one repeats 4 times so you will need 5 different factorials in the denominator. The value for each of those factorials will be 4 as each one repeats exactly 4 times. As a result the formula will look like this: $\frac{20!}{4!4!4!4!4!} = \frac{20!}{(4!)^5}$

5. (E)

The key trigger word in this problem is that it asks for 2 or 3 songs. Once you have noted that K has multiple values, simply calculate each case individually and then sum them together. In this problem, there are 10 songs to choose from so N = 10 and there are either 2 or 3 spots in which to arrange those 10 songs:

N = 10	Possibilities for each case using basic counting skills
K = 3	$10 \cdot 9 \cdot 8 = 720$
K = 2	$10 \cdot 9 \quad = 90$
Sum of the 2 cases	$= 810$

6. (D)

In this difficult "at most" problem you must realize that there are three possible values for K: 1, 2, or 3. In other words, there can be one letter codes, two letter codes, or three letter codes. The question also specifies that you can reuse letters within any one code so it is not a strict permutation. To solve consider each case individually using basic counting principles:

N = 26 (there are 26 letters in the alphabet)

K = 3 $26 \cdot 26 \cdot 26 = 26^3$

K = 2 $26 \cdot 26 = 26^2$

K = 1 $26 = 26$

Sum of three cases   = some number with a unit's digit of 8

Importantly, as on any GMAT question, you should realize that the calculations are too tedious and there must be a shortcut. A quick inspection of the unit's digit of each case before they are summed shows that they must each end in 6. When you add three numbers together that end in 6, the result will always end in eight. As a result, the answer is D, 18,728 – the only answer choice that meets those conditions.

7. **(C)**

In this problem, you must first calculate two different combinations. The first calculation is the number of different groups of 3 women that can be selected from 8 women. N = 8 and K = 3 so the number of possible female groups is: $\frac{8!}{3!(8-3)!} = \frac{8!}{3!5!} = \frac{8 \cdot 7 \cdot 6}{6} = 56$. For the number of male groups N = 5 and K =3 so $\frac{5!}{3!(5-3)!} = \frac{5!}{3!2!} = \frac{5 \cdot 4}{2} = 10$. The difficult part of this question for most students is what to do next. At this point, use your knowledge of basic counting principles and apply them to this problem. The team consists of two parts: women and men. There are 56 choices for female spot and 10 choices for the male spot. The answer is thus $10 \cdot 56$ or 560 different teams. Many students want to add here but that would not be logical. Since you are forming a team that is made up of BOTH the male and female parts, you are including the male subteam AND the female subteam. When you think "AND" you multiply (when you think "or" you add).

8. **(D)**

In this case, note the trigger words "At least one" and find the complementary event to getting at least one red ball, which is getting no red balls. Also, note that the question asks you to pick the balls at the same time, therefore the problem will involve dependent probability (remember, picking at the same time is the same as one at a time without replacement) Finding the probability of no red balls in this case means finding the probability of picking black and then black. On the first pick, the probability of getting a black ball is $\frac{2}{5}$, because there are 2 favorable outcomes out of 5 possible outcomes. In the second pick, the probability has changed and is now $\frac{1}{4}$ because there are now 4 possible outcomes, of which only 1 is favorable. Because we need the probability of black AND black, we multiply the probabilities to get $\frac{2}{20}$ or $\frac{1}{10}$. Importantly, this is not the answer to the question. If the probability of getting no red (black and then black) is $\frac{1}{10}$ then the probability of getting at least one red must be complementary to that or $1 - \frac{1}{10} = \frac{9}{10}$. Answer is D.

Note

This question can also be solved by simply adding up the probabilities of the different ways to get at least one red, but that approach is always more tedious and prone to error on questions such as this. Still, students should understand this approach so let's look at the solution if it is solved without using complementary events.

There are 3 ways to get "at least one red" in this example:

Red and then Black

Black and then Red

Red and then Red

The probability of Red and then Black = $\frac{2}{5} \cdot \frac{3}{4} = \frac{6}{20}$ or $\frac{3}{10}$

As you learned previously, the probability of Black and then Red must be the same as Red and then Black so you do not need to do the work. To prove it again mathematically you see that: P (B and R) $= \frac{3}{5} \cdot \frac{2}{4} = \frac{6}{20}$ or $\frac{3}{10}$

The probability of Red and then Red $= \frac{3}{5} \cdot \frac{2}{4} = \frac{6}{20}$ or $\frac{3}{10}$. The fact that this value is the same as the others is pure coincidence in this one problem.

To get the answer simply sum the probabilities because we are asking for the probability of Red then Black OR Black then Red OR Red then Red and they are mutually exclusive events. As a result the answer is of course the same as what we calculated using complementary events: $\frac{3}{10} + \frac{3}{10} + \frac{3}{10} = \frac{9}{10}$.

9. **(B)**

The first step is to note the trigger words "At least one" and to realize that it is a dependent probability problem (same time = one at a time, without replacement). As a result, the best approach is to find the probability of the complementary event and subtract it from 1. In this case, the complementary event is picking no yellow balls. In the jar, there are 8 yellow balls and 10 non-yellow balls (no need to distinguish between blue and black). The probability of picking non-yellow AND non-yellow in your two picks without replacement is the following: $\frac{10}{18} \cdot \frac{9}{17} = \frac{5}{17}$. Because this is the probability of the complementary event to what the question is asking for (at least one yellow) you must subtract the result from 1. Probability of at least one yellow $= 1 \frac{5}{17} = \frac{12}{17}$. Answer is B.

10. **(D)**

In this question, you must recognize that you are dealing with a pairs probability scenario. Regardless of which bowl you pick from first, you must get one of the colored balls in order to get a pair in the end. As a result, the probability in the first pick is 5 favorable outcomes (one of the colored balls) over 100 total outcomes or $\frac{1}{20}$. On the second pick, you must not only get a colored ball, but also get the exact color that was picked on the first pick. As a result, there will be only one favorable outcome out of the 100 balls so the probability for the second pick is $\frac{1}{100}$. Multiplying these together you get a probability of $\frac{1}{2000}$ so the answer is D.

11. (E)

The only way to solve this question is to determine the probability of getting no pairs, and then subtract that probability from 1. Again, the trigger words on this question to prompt that approach are "at least one". To find the probability of getting no pairs, take each roll individually and consider the approach discussed in the previous pairs problems. For the first roll, it does not matter what you get, so all numbers are favorable and the probability is 1. On the subsequent rolls, you must determine the probability that you DO NOT get a pair. On the second roll, there are 5 favorable outcomes out of 6, because 5 of the numbers will not match the original roll. On the third roll, there are 4 favorable outcomes out of 6, because 4 of the numbers will not match the two numbers that have already been rolled. On the fourth roll, there are 3 favorable outcomes out of 6, because only three of the numbers will not match the first three rolls. As a result the probability of getting no pairs is $\frac{6}{6} \cdot \frac{5}{6} \cdot \frac{4}{6} \cdot \frac{3}{6} = \frac{5}{18}$. As a result, the probability of getting at least one pair is $1 - \frac{5}{18}$ $= \frac{13}{18}$ Answer is E.

12. (B)

This is a hard probability question that must be solved by considering the number of favorable outcomes. As with all binomial problems involving 5 events, the number of total outcomes is 2^5 or 32. So how can you figure out the number of those 32 outcomes that have 3 days in a row of rain? Consider the three scenarios that allow you to have 3 days of rain in a row.

A. Three days of rain and 2 of no rain   RRRNN

B. Four days of rain and 1 of no rain   RRRRN

C. Five days of rain and 0 of no rain   RRRRR

For each scenario you must consider each outcome that is possible.

In scenario A, the following outcomes are favorable: RRRNN, NRRRN, and NNRRR.

Total favorable = 3

In scenario B, the following outcomes are favorable: RRRRN, RRRNR, RNRRR, NRRRR.

Total favorable = 4

In scenario C, there is only one possible outcome and it is favorable: RRRRR.

Total favorable = 1.

Therefore the total number of favorable outcomes is 8 over the total number of outcomes of $32 = \frac{8}{32} = \frac{1}{4}$. Answer is B.

13. **(E)**

Because the balls are being replaced in this problem, it is another classic binomial problem. However, it also contains the "at least one" language so it is best approached by viewing the complementary event. If we want to find the probability of getting "at least one" black ball, it is easier to find the probability of getting no black balls. That probability is simply $(\frac{60}{100})^3$ or $(\frac{6}{10})^3 = \frac{216}{1000} = .216$ As we need the complementary event to that probability we must subtract .216 from 1 = .784. Therefore the probability of getting at least one black ball = .784 and the answer is E.

Assorted Problem Solutions

14. (D)

Since all primes, except for 2, are odd, number N will always be odd. Then, in order for the sum of N + K to be odd, number K must be even. Thus, our task is to find the number of even multiples of 5 between 10 and 40. Because these numbers have to be divisible by 2 and 5, we will be looking for multiples of 10. The fastest way to compute the probability would probably be to list all multiples of 5 between 10 and 40 and then count the number of multiples of 10: 10, 15, 20, 25, 30, 35, 40. We have 4 multiples of 10 among the 7 possibilities for number K. Probability (N + K is odd) = Probability (K is even) = $\frac{4}{7}$.

15. (C)

Since the letter combination is pre-determined, we cannot create any items by changing the letters. Further, since we are dealing with male apparel, the last digit in the 3-digit combination must be even, leaving us with 5 choices for the last digit (0, 2, 4, 6, 8). Because there are no other restrictions, we can use any of the 10 digits (from 0 to 9) in the first and second places of the 3-digit combination. Thus, we have one combination for the letters, 10 combinations for the first digit, 10 combinations for the second digit, and 5 combinations for the third digit. Total number of combinations = $1 \cdot 10 \cdot 10 \cdot 5 = 500$ Alternatively, we know there are 1000 combinations of a 3-digit number (think of it as a number lock on a briefcase): 000, 001, 002 … 997, 998, 999. Since half of these are even, the answer must be 500.

16. (C)

Since the cafeteria is closed on weekends, we have 5 days available for 3 lunches. Since lunch meals are indistinguishable in this scenario, their order does not matter after we the select the lunch days. We can then use the combinations formula to compute the

number of choices. Number of choices for lunch $= \dfrac{5!}{3! \cdot (5\text{-}3)!} = 10$. The similar logic applies

to dinners. The only difference is that Fernando prefers to dine at home on Fridays and

will therefore have 4 rather than 5 days to use his dinner admission. Number of choices for

dinner $= \dfrac{4!}{3! \cdot (4\text{-}3)!} = 4$. Number of choices for all meals $= 4 \cdot 10 = 40$.

17. **(E)**

Since only the first 3 teams are ranked in the competition, the number of outcomes will

equal the number of ways in which the top 3 teams can be selected from the pool of 6.

Since changing the order of the top 3 teams (e.g. switching the first and second places)

creates a new outcome, we are dealing with permutations. Thus, we can compute the

number of outcomes by using the permutations formula:

Number of outcomes $= \dfrac{6!}{(6\text{-}3)!} = 120$.

18. **(B)**

In this scenario, the number of outcomes will simply be the number of ways the top three

teams can be arranged. This is equal to $3! = 6$.

19. **(D)**

This is a permutations-with-restrictions problem. Without the restriction, the number

of permutations involved is120, as in #4 above. A good way to solve this question is to

determine the number of permutations that do not satisfy the restriction and subtract that

number from 120. For an outcome not to satisfy the restriction, A must be ranked and B

must not be ranked. A can be ranked in any of the 3 spots. Since B cannot be ranked, there

are 4 teams available to fill the other two spots: $\dfrac{4!}{(4\text{-}2)!} = 12$. Multiply 12 by 3 to get 36

permutations that are not allowed.120 - 36 = 84.

20. (C)

To calculate the number of possible color arrangements, we need to find the number of 4-element permutations that can be created from a pool of 4 elements. In other words, we need to find the number of ways in which we can rearrange the 4 colors. Since two of the shirts are of the same color, we have 2 repeating elements and can apply the formula for permutations with repeating elements: Number of color combinations $= \frac{4!}{2!} = 12$.

21. (D)

This problem can be solved by finding the difference between the total number of two-element subsets and the number that contains both 2 and 4. There is only one two-element subset that contains both 2 and 4. The total number of two-element subsets is $\frac{(4)(3)}{2} = 6$; therefore the difference is five. Thus, the answer is D. Alternately, the two element subsets of $\{1, 2, 3, 4\}$ are $\{1, 2\}, \{1, 3\}, \{1, 4\}, \{2, 3\}, \{2, 3\}$ and $\{3, 4\}$. There are 5 two-element subsets that do not contain both 2 and 4.

22. (B)

It is sometimes a good idea to look at the answer choices before tackling the problem. For example, if 4 colors were used, 4 centers could be identified with a single color and $_4C_2 = \frac{4!}{2!2!} = 6$ centers could be identified with two colors. Thus, only 10 centers could be identified with 4 colors. Similarly, with 5 colors, 5 centers could be identified with a single color and $_5C_2 = \frac{5!}{2!3!} = \frac{(5)(4)}{2} = 10$. Centers could be identified with two colors for a total of 15. Therefore, a minimum of 5 colors is needed, and the answer is B.

23. (D)

Think of a key chain as seven locations, with the possibilities decreasing each time a key is assigned to a location: $\underline{7} \times \underline{6} \times \underline{5} \times \underline{4} \times \underline{3} \times \underline{2} \times \underline{1}$

However, since a key chain is circular, the first and the last keys are adjacent, so each combination is repeated 7 times. For example:

#1: <u>A - B - C - D - E - F - G</u>

#2: <u>B - C - D - E - F - G - A</u>

#3: <u>C - D - E - F - G - A - B</u>

#4: <u>D - E - F - G - A - B - C</u>

#5: <u>E - F - G - A - B - C - D</u>

#6: <u>F - G - A - B - C - D - E</u>

#7: <u>G - A - B - C - D - E - F</u>

Each example, #1- #7, is the same, when arranged in a keychain, because the last spot is next to the first spot. Since each combination is repeated seven times, the normal calculation for number of combinations must be divided by 7: $\frac{7!}{7} = \frac{7 \cdot 6 \cdot 5 \cdot 4 \cdot 3 \cdot 2 \cdot 1}{7} =$ $6 \cdot 5 \cdot 4 \cdot 3 \cdot 2 \cdot 1 = 6!$ Alternatively, a circular arrangement with x elements is simplified as having the following possibilities: $(x - 1)! = (7 - 1)!$

24. **(E)**

In the first set, 7 and 11 are the two prime numbers, so the probability of x being prime is $\frac{2}{5}$. In the second set, 23 is the only prime number, so the probability of y being prime is $\frac{1}{4}$. Both choices are random and independent, so multiply the two probabilities to find the probability that both x and y are prime: $\frac{2}{5} \cdot \frac{1}{4} = \frac{2}{20} = \frac{1}{10}$.

25. **(E):** As in #11, in the first set the probability of x being prime is $\frac{2}{5}$. Since y and z are each unique numbers, their selection is not independent – the outcome of one influences the other. It does not matter which variable you begin with, so let's begin with y. As in #11, since 23 is the only prime number the probability of y being prime is $\frac{1}{4}$. If y is 23, z can only be 20, 21, or 22. Therefore z must be non-prime, and the overall probability is $\frac{2}{5} \cdot \frac{1}{4} = \frac{2}{20} = \frac{1}{10}$, just as in #11.

26. **(A)**

There are 7 even numbers in the set. Since 3 spots are being chosen for 7 numbers, and the order is irrelevant (a subset of {1,2,3} is the same as {2,1,3}), this is a combination:

$_7C_3 = \dfrac{7!}{3!(7\text{-}3)!} = \dfrac{7!}{3! \cdot 4!}$. **Note:** The answer is not calculated out.

27. (B)

Each exterior color can correspond with a different interior color.

Therefore, there are $7 \cdot 6 = 42$ possible color combinations.

28. (A)

In each spot, one number or letter can be placed. This allows $10 + 26 = 36$ different possibilities for each location. For a license plate with 6 digits, there are 36 possibilities 6 times, providing the following number of combinations: $36 \cdot 36 \cdot 36 \cdot 36 \cdot 36 \cdot 36 = 36^6$.

29. (D)

To get a flush, you need 5 cards from the same suit. Each suit has 13 different cards, so we need to find "13 choose 5" (i.e. how many different ways are there draw 5 things from 13?).

$$\dfrac{13!}{5!(13\text{-}5)!} = \dfrac{13 \cdot 12 \cdot 11 \cdot 10 \cdot 9}{5 \cdot 4 \cdot 3 \cdot 2 \cdot 1}$$

Since there are 4 suits, to get the total number of ways to draw a flush, we need to multiply this expression by 4.

$$\dfrac{4 \cdot 13 \cdot 12 \cdot 11 \cdot 10 \cdot 9}{5 \cdot 4 \cdot 3 \cdot 2 \cdot 1} = \dfrac{4 \cdot 13 \cdot 11 \cdot 9}{1} = 143 \cdot 4 \cdot 9 = 572 \cdot 9 = 5720 - 572 = 5148$$

30. (D)

Place a man anywhere. To his right we have a choice of 10 women. To her right we have a choice of 9 men. To the second man's right we have the choice of 9 women…

$10 \cdot 9 \cdot 9 \cdot 8 \cdot 8 \cdot 7 \cdot 7 \ldots \cdot 2 \cdot 2 \cdot 1 \cdot 1$. The reason the first choice of man is not counted is because the table is circular, hence his position is irrelevant.

Combinatorics & Probability

31. **(D)**

Any one of the 3 boys could be seated in the first seat, either of the remaining 2 boys in the third seat, and the remaining boy in the fifth seat. Thus there are 3(2)(1) = 6 ways the boys could be arranged. There are also 3 girls to be arranged in 3 seats; thus, by the same reasoning, there are 6 ways in which the girls can be arranged. Since for each arrangement of the boys, there are 6 arrangements of the girls, there are 6(6) = 36 ways in which the 3 boys and the 3 girls can be arranged.

32. **(D)**

There are 4 different numbers (*x*) that can be chosen from {1, 2, 3, 4} and 3 different numbers (*y*) that can be chosen from {5, 6, 7}. Therefore, the number of different pairs of numbers *x* and *y* that can be chosen is 4 · 3, or 12. Note that if *xy* is to be even, at least one of *x* and *y* must be even. If *x* is even, then *y* can be odd or even. Since there are 2 even values of *x*, there are 2 · 3 = 6 possibilities that *xy* will be even. If *x* is odd, then *y* must be even. Since there is 1 even value of *y* and 2 odd values of *x*, there are 2 · 1 = 2 additional possibilities. Thus, there are 6 + 2 = 8 possibilities for *xy* to be even, and the probability that *xy* will be even is $\frac{8}{12} = \frac{2}{3}$.

33. **(B)**

The number of possible selections from A is 4, and the number of possible selections from B is 5. Therefore, the number of different pairs of numbers, one from A and one from B, is 4 · 5 = 20. Of these 20 pairs of numbers, there are 4 possible pairs that sum to 9, namely: 2 and 7, 3 and 6, 4 and 5, and 5 and 4. Therefore, the probability that the sum of the 2 integers selected will equal 9 is $\frac{4}{20}$ or 0.20.

34. **(C)**

The easiest approach to this problem is to use what you learned about permutations with repeating elements. In other words, we need to find the number of ways in which we can rearrange the 6 results taking into account that we have 3 repeating elements of wins and 2 repeating elements of losses. Number of ways to end the season $= \frac{6!}{3! \cdot 2!} = 60$. Alternatively, when we are dealing with multiple selections from a group, it is helpful to consider these selections sequentially, starting with one of the groups and then allocating the remaining elements to other groups. Since switching the games within the "won" group or the "lost" group does not create a new arrangement, we will be using the combinations formula.

Number of ways to win 3 games out of 6: $\frac{6!}{3! \cdot (6\text{-}3)!} = 20$

Number of ways to end 1 game in a draw from the remaining 3: 3

Number of ways to lose 2 games from the remaining 2: 1

(you can also check this with a general formula: $\frac{2!}{2!(2!\text{-}2!)} = \frac{2!}{2!(0!)} = 1$)

Total number of ways to end the season: $20 \cdot 3 \cdot 1 = 60$

35. (B)

Since set X consists of an even number of terms, its median is equal to the average of the two middle numbers, where the elements are arranged in the ascending order:

Median of set X $= \frac{3+7}{2} = 5$. Since after an additional element is added to set X, it will have an odd number of terms, we know that the median of the new set will be the middle element, if the terms of the set are arranged in order. Because we are limited to single-digit integers, the numbers that will increase the median of the set include 6, 7, 8, and 9. In order for the range of set X to remain the same, the greatest and the smallest values in the set must remain the same. In other words, the new number must be between 2 and 8, inclusive. By combining both conditions, we know that the numbers that will increase the median without affecting the range are 6, 7, and 8. Since there are 10 non-negative single-digit integers, the probability to select one of these 3 numbers is $\frac{3}{10}$ or 30%.

36. (B)

Since the President and Vice President cannot be separated, we can treat them as one unit

and treat the other members of the Board as one unit each. Thus, we will have 5 units that will need to be allocated among 5 places. Since the seating patterns can be created only by rearranging the units, the number of such rearrangements is equal to 5! or 120. Since we can switch the places of the President and Vice President, we will have 2 possibilities for each arrangement of the units. Total number of arrangements = 2 · 5! = 240.

37. **(A)**

Because all multiples of 5 end with a 5 or 0, those of them that end with a 0 will also be divisible by 10. Since we need to exclude the numbers divisible by 10, we need to find the number of 3-digit integers ending with a 5. Because the first digit in any three-digit number cannot be 0, we have 9 choices for the first digit. The middle digit can be any of the 10 digits, while the last digit has to be 5. Thus, we have 9 choices for the first digit, 10 choices for the second digit and 1 choice for the third digit. Number of 3-digit numbers fitting the criteria = 9 · 10 · 1 = 90

38. **(C)**

Since the order in which the roses of the same color are selected by Jeremy does not matter, we are dealing with combinations. We can use the combinations formula to compute the number of 3-element selections from a pool of 6 elements (red roses) and 4 elements (white roses).

Number of choices for a red-rose bunch $= \dfrac{6!}{(6\text{-}3)! \cdot 3!} = 20$

Number of choices for a white-rose bunch $= \dfrac{4!}{(4\text{-}3)! \cdot 3!} = 4$

Ratio of choices for red roses to white roses $= \dfrac{20}{4} = 5{:}1$

Combinatorics Solutions

39. (A)

Because changing the order of the questions does not create a new exam, we are in the world of combinations. To answer the question, we need to compute the number of 3-element unordered selections that can be created from a pool of 5 elements.

Number of 3-question exams $= \dfrac{5!}{3!(5\text{-}3)!} = 10$

40. (B)

Since there are no ties in a running competition, the number of outcomes is equal to the number of ways to assign the 5 athletes to places from first to fifth. In other words, the total number of outcomes is equal to the number of ways to rearrange the 5 runners from best to worst. The number of rearrangements that can be created from 5 elements is equal to 5! or 120.

41. (C)

Since switching the order of selected books does not create a new selection, we need to use the combinations formula: Number of possible selections $= \dfrac{6!}{3!(6\text{-}3)!} = 20$.

42. (B)

Since no chemical may be assigned the same 3 colors as another, a mere rearrangement of these colors will not enable us to mark another chemical. Therefore, the order does not matter and we are dealing with combinations. We can find the number of 3-element unordered selections from the pool of 8 elements by using the combinations formula:

Number of color combinations $= \dfrac{7!}{3!(7\text{-}3)!} = 35$.

43. **(C)**

Because the securities need to be ranked, the order matters and we are dealing with permutations. Our task is to find the number of three-element ordered selections that can be created from the pool of 7 elements: Number of top-three lists $= \frac{7!}{(7-3)!} = 210$

44. **(C)**

Because changing the order of letters creates a new arrangement, the order matters and we are dealing with permutations. We can find the number of rearrangements that can be created from a pool of 5 elements, 2 of which are the same (two T's), using the permutations formula for sets with repeating elements:

Number of 5-letter combinations $= \frac{5!}{2!} = 3 \cdot 4 \cdot 5 = 60$.

45. **(B)**

Since each number in the code must be a single-digit prime, the suitable digits are 2, 3, 5 and 7. Since no digit can be repeated, we have 4 elements to fill the 3 spots and can find the number of different codes from the permutations formula:

Number of ID codes $= \frac{4!}{(4-3)!} = 24$.

46. **(D)**

On problems that involve selections at multiple stages, it is often helpful to consider each step in the decision process individually and then compute the number of possibilities for each step and the total number of possible combinations.

Pizza flavor – 4 possibilities

Extra cheese – 2 possibilities (extra cheese/no extra cheese)

Mushrooms – 2 possibilities (mushrooms/no mushrooms)

Since extra cheese or mushrooms can be added to any flavor of the pizza, we can find the total number of varieties by multiplying the combinations for each of the 3 steps: Total number of varieties $= 4 \cdot 2 \cdot 2 = 16$

47. **(E)**

From the given percentages, we know that there are 3 novels, 2 study guides and 3 textbooks. Since each book is different, switching the order creates a new arrangement and we are dealing with permutations. Further, note that since we have to display all items, the new arrangements can be created only by rearranging books. The number of rearrangements in each group can be found as the factorial of the number of elements. Number of rearrangements for novels: $3! = 6$. Number of rearrangements for study guides: $2! = 2$. Number of rearrangements for textbooks: $3! = 6$. **Note:** We cannot simply multiply all the arrangements in each group to get the final number of possibilities. This would be the case if we could not move the categories of books on the shelf, i.e. if, for example, the novels had to appear first followed by the study guides and textbooks. Since we are not precluded from moving the categories of books on the shelf, we can create new arrangements by rearranging the groups. Since we have 3 categories, let's find the number of ways to move them around: Number of arrangements of the 3 categories of books: $3! = 6$. Total number of book arrangements: $6 \cdot 2 \cdot 6 \cdot 6 = 2 \cdot 6^3 = 2 \cdot 216 = 432$

48. **(B)**

First, let's find out how many different arrangements of students are possible. Since we can only reshuffle students among the 5 seats, there are a total of 5! or 120 arrangements. Since Bob and Lisa must have only one neighbor from the group, they need to occupy seats 1 and 5 or seats 5 and 1, respectively. The remaining 3 students can take any of the 3 seats left in the middle, creating a total of 3! or 6 arrangements. We can also sit Bob and Lisa in two ways (Bob in the left seat and Lisa in the right and vice versa) for each of the arrangements of the 3 students in the middle. Number of arrangements with Bob and Lisa at the opposite ends: $2 \cdot 3! = 12$. Total number of arrangements: $5! = 120$. Probability to sit Bob and Lisa at the opposite ends: $\frac{12}{120} = 10\%$.

Probability Solutions

49. **(E)**

The quickest way to solve this problem is to use the One Mirror strategy. The complementary event to "at least one of the two students is interested in investment banking" (let's call this event A) is "none of the two students is interested in investment banking" (event B). Then, in order for event B to occur, each of the selected students must not be interested in banking. Since we know that there are 21 students, among whom 6 are not interested in banking ($\frac{2}{7}$ of 21), we can compute the probability for event B: $P(B) = \frac{6}{21} \cdot \frac{5}{20} = \frac{2}{7} \cdot \frac{1}{4} = \frac{1}{14}$. Since we constructed event B to be complementary to event A, we can easily find the probability of event A: $P(A) = 1 - P(B) = 1 - \frac{1}{14} = \frac{13}{14}$.

50. **(A)**

This problem can be solved without any computational work. We know that a multiple of 6 is always even and that any two-digit prime number is odd. Adding an even number to an odd will always yield an odd integer. Since an odd integer is not divisible by 2, reducing the result by half will never yield an integer. Thus, regardless of how many times the operation is repeated, the probability to get an integer is 0.

51. **(D)**

Since 89 is divisible only by 1 and 89, we are looking for a number with only two factors, i.e. a prime. To find the probability of selecting a prime, we need to count the number of primes between 50 and 69 and then divide it by the total number of integers between 50 and 69, inclusive. The total number of integers between 50 and 69 = 69 − 50 + 1 = 20. Note that after we found that there are 20 integers, we can eliminate answers B and C because these percentages of 20 will not yield a whole number. Now, let's count the number of primes between 50 and 69. The quickest way to do this is to write out the 20 integers and then cross out all even numbers, multiples of 3, and multiples of 5. We are left with 53, 59, 61 and 67. Then, we only need to check their divisibility by 7. There is no need to check whether the four numbers are divisible by 11, 13 and other primes because, for instance, 11 or 13 could go into these integers only about 5 times, and we have already eliminated all numbers between 50 and 69 divisible by smaller primes. Thus, we have 4 primes among the 20 integers. Probability to select a prime $= \frac{4}{20} = 20\%$.

52. **(C)**

First, we need to find the number of launches that will occur in the next 16 months. Since it is currently January, 12 months from today will also be January and 16 months from today will be May (1st month + 4 = 5th month). Thus, three shuttle launches (2 in June + 1 in October) will be made in within this period. To find the probability that at least one launch will be delayed (event A), we can apply the One Mirror Strategy and construct the complementary event B "none of the three launches are delayed." We can then compute the probabilities using the AND formula and then applying the properties of complementary events:

P(B) = P(first launch on time) · P(second launch on time) · P(third launch on time)

$= \frac{9}{10} \cdot \frac{9}{10} \cdot \frac{9}{10} = \frac{729}{1000}$

$P(A) = 1 - P(B) = 1 - \frac{729}{1000} = \frac{271}{1000}$

53. **(A)**

For the product of the three dice to be an odd number, all of the dice must produce an odd number (1, 3 or 5). Additionally, since this product must be divisible by 25, at least 2 of the dice must yield 5. Thus, two dice must yield a 5 and the remaining dice can yield 1, 3 or 5. If we mark the dice as first, second, and third, 7 outcomes will suit us: 5-5-5 5-5-3 5-3-5 3-5-5 5-5-1 5-1-5 1-5-5. Total number of outcomes is $6 \cdot 6 \cdot 6 = 216$. According to the definition, the probability to get one of the suitable outcomes is $\frac{7}{216}$.

54. **(E)**

In order for Bob to dial the correct number in at most two attempts, he must find it either in his first attempt or in his second attempt. Thus, there are two possible scenarios: (1) The first attempt is successful and the number is found; (2) The first attempt is unsuccessful AND the second attempt is successful. To find these probabilities, we need to compute the total number of possibilities for the remaining two digits. Since these digits cannot be 0, 1, 2, 5 or 7, we have 5 choices left for each of the two digits (3, 4, 6, 8, or 9).

Total number of possibilities = $5 \cdot 5 = 25$.

Probability (scenario 1) = Probability (first attempt is successful) = $\frac{1}{25}$

Probability (scenario 2) = Probability (first attempt is unsuccessful) $\cdot$ Probability (second attempt is successful) = $\frac{24}{25} \cdot \frac{1}{24} = \frac{1}{25}$

Note: If the first attempt is unsuccessful in scenario 2, we will be able to eliminate one combination of digits and will have 24 rather than 25 possibilities before the second attempt. Probability to guess the number in at most 2 attempts = Probability (Scenario 1 OR Scenario 2) = $\frac{1}{25} + \frac{1}{25} = \frac{2}{25}$. We can rewrite this to fit the answer choices: $\frac{50}{625}$.

55. **(D)**

Since 5 is not divisible by 8, in order for $\frac{5N^3}{8}$ to be an integer, N^3 must be divisible by 8. Note that for N^3 to be divisible by 8, it is sufficient that N be an even integer – any even integer is a multiple of 2 and consequently $N \cdot N \cdot N$ is a multiple of $2 \cdot 2 \cdot 2 = 8$. N = 0 is a special case, but it also results in an integer – 0. Since we are dealing only with non-negative single-digit numbers, there are 5 even integers (0, 2, 4, 6, 8) among the 10 numbers. We have all the information to compute the probability:

Probability of selecting an even integer = $\frac{5}{10} = \frac{1}{2} = 50\%$

56. **(C)**

In order to David to submit no more than 2 applications, he must be accepted either this year or next year. Thus, there are two possible scenarios:

(1)   Admission granted this year;

                OR

(2)   Admission declined this year AND admission granted next year

Using the OR and AND formulas, we can compute the probability of admission within the next 2 years in the following steps:

P(scenario 1) = 15%

P(scenario 2) = P(decline as a first-time applicant) · P(admission as a re-applicant)

= (1-15%) · 20% = 17%

P(admission within 2 years) = P(scenario 1 OR scenario 2) = 15% + 17% = 32%

57. **(C)**

To be a multiple of 45, the number has to be divisible by 9 and 5. The single-digit positive multiples of 3 are 3, 6 and 9. Since none of them is divisible by 5, the prime number in the product must be a multiple of 5. Since the only prime divisible by 5 is 5, the prime number must equal 5. Since we will not get any factors of 3 from the prime number 5, divisibility by 9 has to be ensured by the 3 multiples of 3. Because only 9 is divisible by 9, we know that the only pair that will satisfy the condition in the problem is 9 and 5. Finally, to find the probability, we need to compute the total number of possible cases. If we write out the prime numbers less than 20 (they are 2, 3, 5 ,7 ,11, 13, 17 and 19), we can see that there are 8 of them. We also know that there are 3 possibilities for the single-digit multiple of 3. Therefore, there are 24 total possibilities. Since only two pairs satisfy the condition, the probability to get a multiple of 45 is $\frac{1}{24}$.

Data Sufficiency Solutions

58. (A)

From statement (1) we know that selecting a white ball is twice as likely as selecting a ball of any other color, which is sufficient to find the probability of selecting a white ball. If you would like to verify this, here is a quick illustration. If we denote the number of non-white balls as x, the number of white balls is $2x$ and the total number of balls is $3x$:

Probability to select a white ball $= \frac{2x}{3x} = \frac{2}{3}$. Statement (1) alone is sufficient. From statement (2) we know only the difference between the number of white balls and balls of other colors. This is insufficient to determine the actual number of balls or the ratio of white balls to total balls that would be necessary to find the probability. Intuitively, you can see that there can be 31 white balls and 1 ball of another color (probability $= \frac{31}{32}$) or 60 white balls and 30 balls of other colors (probability $= \frac{2}{3}$). Therefore, the second statement is insufficient and the answer is A.

59. (C)

Statement (1) tells us that there are 9 age categories at the conference but does not provide us with any information about the participating schools. Thus, this statement is insufficient. Statement (2) tells us that there are 10 categories for schools but gives no information about the age of the participants. By combining the two statements together, we know that we can create a maximum of 90 distinct combinations of age/school (9 choices for age · 10 choices for school). Since we have 100 participants and only 90 different combinations, some of the attendees must have the same combination, i.e. must represent the same school and be of the same age.

60. (B)

To answer the question, we need to find the number of gyms that have both a pool and a squash court. Statement (1) does not tell us anything about the number of gyms with a pool and is therefore insufficient to answer the question. From statement (2), we learn that there are 9 gyms with a pool and that each of them is equipped with a squash court. Therefore, there are 9 gyms that have both amenities. Note that the total number of gyms that have a squash court is not needed, since only those of them that have a pool will qualify.

61. (B)

To find the number of team combinations, we need to know the number of eligible candidates and the number of slots on the team. Statement (1) simply gives us the relationship between these two values and is therefore insufficient to find the number of combinations. Intuitively, you can see that if there are 2 people on the team and 6 candidates, the number of combinations is much smaller than if there are 10 people on the team and 30 eligible candidates. From statement (2), we know that we have 12 candidates to fill the 4 spots on the team; In other words, statement (2) provides us both with the size of the pool and the size of the selection, thus locking in one value for the number of possible combinations ($\frac{12!}{(12-4)! \cdot 4!}$). Therefore, statement (2) alone is sufficient.

62. (A)

Since Set A contains an odd number of terms, the median of the set will be the number in the middle of the set, if the terms are arranged in ascending or descending order, i.e. the third largest number in the set. To answer the question, we need to find the third largest number in the set. From statement (1), if N^6 is even, N must also be even. Since N is a prime number, we know that N = 2, the only even prime. Thus, the elements of Set A arranged in ascending order are {-9, -8, 2, 4, 15} and the median of the set is 2. Statement (1) alone is sufficient. From statement (2), we know that N < 3. This information alone is insufficient to answer the question. For example, if N = 2, then the median of the set is 2, while if N = -10, then the elements of the set are {-10, -9, -8, 4, 15} and the median of the set is -8.

63. **(C)**

To find the probability that the first selected marble is black, we need to know only the proportion of the black marbles in the jar after the new marbles are added. However, after the first black marble is selected, the number of all marbles (T) and the number of black marbles (B) will be each reduced by 1. In other words, the probability that the second marble will be black after the first marble was black will be equal to $\frac{B-1}{T-1}$. To find this probability, we need to know the exact values of the total number of marbles and the number of black marbles (for instance, $\frac{5-1}{10-1}$ is different from $\frac{50-1}{100-1}$). Statement (1) does not provide us with any information about the exact number of marbles in the jar. While the ratio of the black marbles is sufficient to compute the probability that the first selected marble is black, it is insufficient to find the probability that the second selected marble is also black. Statement (1) alone is insufficient. Statement (2) provides us with the information about the number of black marbles added but gives no information on the total number of marbles in the jar and is therefore insufficient. If we combine the two statements, we know that the 8 black marbles in the jar constitute 50% of all marbles and that there are a total of 16 marbles in the jar. Since we know the total number of marbles and the number of black marbles, we can answer the question. Statements (1) and (2) taken together are sufficient to answer the question.

64. **(B)**

Since the number of seats is equal to the number of students, we need to find the number of ways in which the students can be rearranged within one row – the value equal to N! In other words, we simply need to find N. From statement (1), we get two simple equations:

|N - 6| = 3

N - 6 = 3 or N - 6 = -3

N = 9 or N = 3

Since we have two solutions, both of which are positive and could represent the number of students, we cannot give a definitive answer to the question. Statement (1) alone is insufficient. From statement (2), we get a quadratic equation:

N2= 7N + 18

N2 - 7N -18 = 0

(N - 9)(N + 2) =0

N= 9 OR N = -2

Since the number of students cannot be negative, only N = 9 fits the problem stem. We have one value for the number of students and statement (2) is sufficient to answer the question.

65. **(D)**

The probability that it will rain on each of the 3 days (day 1 AND day 2 AND day 3) is equal to the product of the individual probabilities of rain on each day ($p1 \cdot p2 \cdot p3$). Since the probability of rain is the same for each of the 3 days and is not affected by the outcomes of other days (independent), the probability that it will rain every day is simply p^3, where p is the probability of rain on any single day. Thus, to answer the question we simply need to find the probability of rain on any single day. Since statement (2) is simpler, this is a good start for your analysis. Statement (2) provides us with the information on the probability of rain on one single day and is therefore sufficient to answer the question. Statement (1) provides us with the information about the probability of two dry days in a row. Since the events "a dry day" and "a rainy day" are mutually exclusive, the probability to have no rain on any single day is $1 - p$, where p is the probability of rain on any single day, as we noted earlier. Since we are given the information about the first and the second days being dry, we can construct an equation and solve it for p, thus answering the question:

P(no rain on day 1 AND no rain on day 2) = $(1 - p)(1 - p) = 0.36$

$$(1 - p)^2 = 0.36$$

$$p = 0.4$$

Each statement alone is sufficient to answer the question.

66. **(E)**

To find the mean of the set, we need to determine the values of K, L and M or their sum. Since K, L and M have to be consecutive positive integers less than 5 (the set is arranged in ascending order and includes only different terms), K, L and M can be either 1, 2 and 3 or 2, 3 and 4. From statement (1), we know that both $2 \cdot 3 \cdot 4$ and $1 \cdot 2 \cdot 3$ will be multiples of 6. Note that any product of 3 positive consecutive integers is a multiple of 6. Since there is at least one even number among any 3 consecutive integers, their product will always be divisible by 2. Further, since 3 consecutive integers go at the step of 3, one of them will always be a multiple of 3 and their product will always be divisible by 3. Since the product is divisible by 2 and 3, it will be divisible by 6. Statement (1) provides no new information about K, L and M and is therefore insufficient. From statement (2), we know that K, L and M can either be 2, 3 and 4, or 1, 2, and 3, since both sequences contain two prime numbers. Statement (2) provides no new information about K, L and M and is therefore insufficient.

67. **(B)**

Statement (1) tells us that a refined number must be a multiple of 22. Note, however, that this is a necessary but not sufficient condition for a refined number. In other words, while every refined number is a multiple of 22, every multiple of 22 is not necessarily a refined number. Since we have no other information about the definition of a refined number, we cannot determine how many integers from 1 to 1000 fit that definition. Statement (2) provides us with a definition of a refined number – a refined number is defined as an even multiple of 11. Since we can find the number of even multiples of 11 in the set, this information is sufficient to answer the question.

Challenge Solutions

68. **(B)**

To find the percentage change in the mean, we need to find the new mean, or more precisely, determine which two elements are dropped. Statement (1) tells us only that the middle number in the set will remain 0. This is insufficient to determine which elements are dropped. For instance, dropping -10 and 7 or -8 and 6, would satisfy the condition in the statement. From statement (2), we know that the range of the set will change. Thus, the smallest value or the largest value or both of them must be among the elements dropped. Upon closer analysis, you can see that only dropping both the smallest and the largest value will give us the desired decrease in range – from 17 (7 - (-10)) to 14 (6 - (-8)). Therefore, statement (2) alone is sufficient.

69. **(D)**

Since changing the order in which the photos are put in the envelope does not result in a new group of photos, the order in which the photos are placed does not matter and we are dealing with combinations. Because Veronica can choose to send either 3 or 4 photos, the total number of possibilities can be found by calculating the number of 3-element combinations and the number of 4-element combinations and then adding the two together:

Number of 3-photo selections $= \dfrac{5!}{(5 - 3)! \cdot 3!} = 10$

Number of 4-photo selections $= \dfrac{5!}{(5 - 4)4! \cdot 4!} = 5$

Total number of possible photo selections $= 10 + 5 = 15$

70. **(D)**

To answer the question, we need to find the number of ways to divide the 7 members of the parliament into groups of 5 (supporters) and 2 (opponents). Since changing the

order of members in each group does not create a new voting pattern (they still remain within supporters or opponents), we can use the combinations formula. Note that the most efficient way to separate a group into two other unordered groups is to find the number of ways to form the smaller group. After the small group has been selected, all the remaining candidates have to be in the other group. In other words, to find the total number of voting patterns, we can simply determine the number of ways in which the 2 opponents can be selected from a group of 7. The remaining 5 members will automatically become the supporters of the proposition. Note that this is valid only because the order is not important and hence there is only 1 way to fill the 5 opponent slots with the 5 remaining candidates. Number of voting patterns = Number of ways to select 2 opponents $= \frac{7!}{2!(7-2)!} = 21$

71. (B)

To simplify the solution of problems involving multiple steps, it is often helpful to consider each of them individually. Let's find the number of choices the company has in each region. Note that the order in which the allocations are made does not matter – i.e. choosing New York and then Boston is the same as choosing Boston and then New York. Thus we will need to use the combinations formula to find the number of possible allocations.

East coast: 2 slots and 3 candidates (Boston, New York and D.C.)

Number of possibilities $= \frac{3!}{2!(3-2)!} = 3$

Midwest: 1 slot and 1 candidate

Number of possibilities $= 1$

West coast: 2 slots and 3 candidates (Seattle, San Francisco and L.A.)

Number of possibilities $= \frac{3!}{2!(3-2)!} = 3$

Total number of possible allocations $= 3 \cdot 1 \cdot 3 = 9$

72. **(D)**

Since the couples cannot be separated, we can consider each couple one unit and simply find the number of ways to rearrange the 3 units. The number of rearrangements that can be created with 3 elements is equal 3! or 6. Note, however, that each couple can also position in 2 different ways: man on the left and woman on the right or vice versa. Since each couple can be rearranged in this way, the number of such rearrangements = $2 \cdot 2 \cdot 2 = 8$. Total number of rearrangements = $6 \cdot 8 = 48$.

73. **(A)**

Since we need exactly 3 tails, the remaining 3 coins must show heads. You can then view the question as allocating 3 heads and 3 tails to six spots. Because all the tails have to occur in a row, we can consider them one unit. Since each of the remaining heads can take any spot, we will consider each of the remaining heads a unit. Thus, we have 4 units to allocate among the 4 spots (1 long spot for tails and 3 for heads). Moreover, 3 of the units are exactly the same; heads are indistinguishable from each other. Thus, we need to compute the number of rearrangements of 4 elements, among which 3 are the same: Number of different sequences $= \frac{4!}{3!} = 4$. Note, however, that since this problem is very restrictive and therefore will have few possibilities fitting the description, solving it graphically may be even more time-efficient. While formulas usually have lower chance of leaving out possible outcomes, this particular problem can also be solved quickly by mapping out the sequences fitting the criteria:

(1) TTTHHH   (2) HTTTHH   (3) HHTTTH   (4) HHHTTT

Thus, there are 4 possible sequences.

74. **(C)**

Statement (1) provides us with enough information to compute the original mean M of set X, but provides us with no information about the new mean. Therefore, statement (1) alone is insufficient. Statement (2) alone is insufficient because we have one equation

with two unknowns and have no way of finding either Z or N. However, plugging the
information from statements (1) into statement (2) coupled with the knowledge of the
original mean M calculated from statement (1), we can find the value of N and hence the
percentage increase of the mean.

$$\text{Average before} = \frac{-14 - 12 + 17 + 28 + 41 + Z}{6} = \frac{-14 - 12 + 17 + 28 + 41 + 60}{6} = 20$$

$$N = \frac{60}{20} = 3$$

$$\text{Average after} = \frac{3(-14) + 3(-12) + 3\cdot 17 + 3\cdot 41 + 3\cdot 60}{6} = 60$$

Percentage increase = 200%

Note that if we know N, we do not need to know the value of Z to find the new mean:

$$\text{Average before} = \frac{-14 - 12 + 17 + 28 + 41 + Z}{6}$$

$$\text{Average after} = \frac{3(-14) + 3(-12) + 3\cdot 17 + 3\cdot 28 + 3\cdot 41 + 3\cdot Z}{6} =$$

$$3(\frac{-14 - 12 + 17 + 28 + 41 + Z}{6}) = 3\cdot \text{Average before}$$

If this were not a data sufficiency question, it would be important to note that while
the mean after is three times the mean before, the percentage increase is 200%. As an
example, think of a company's profit growing by 100% from one year to the next; we say it
has doubled – or that it is two times as great.

75. **(D)**

Since each flag has to include 3 of the 5 national colors and the order in which the colors
are placed matters, we need to find the number of 3-element ordered arrangements
that can be created from a pool of 5 elements. This number will represent the number of
possible flags for a determined position of the stripes (either vertical or horizontal). Let's
assume that first all the stripes are placed horizontally and find the number of flags with
horizontal stripes: Number of flags with horizontal stripes $= \frac{5!}{(5 - 3)!} = 60$. Since the stripes
can appear either horizontally or vertically, we can create one vertical "twin" for every
horizontal color combination simply by changing the horizontal placement into vertical,
while keeping the relative position of all colors the same. Since we will be able to create
one twin for each horizontal color combination, the opportunity to choose the location

of the stripes will double the total number of possible flags: Number of possible flags with horizontal or vertical stripes $= 60 \cdot 2 = 120$

76. (D)

Since the number of elements is small, an efficient way to solve this problem is to find the number of possibilities to fill each of the 3 digit slots and then multiply all the possibilities to get the total number of feasible codes. Furthermore, since there is a constraint on the product of the 3 digits, we will need to reduce the total number of arrangements by the number of possibilities that violate the constraint. If we did not have the additional constraint on the product of the three digits, we would have 3 possibilities for each of the 3 spots in the area code (each of the 3 digits can be used in any spot because they can be repeated). Without the constraint, the total number of codes $= 3 \cdot 3 \cdot 3 = 27$. Now, we need to subtract the number of possibilities that violate the constraint. Since the product of the 3 numbers will be odd only if all the digits are odd, the only code that violates the constraint is 555. Note that any other code containing at least one 2 or 4 will always yield an even product. Number of codes yielding an even product $= 27 - 1 = 26$

77. (D)

Since the order in which the job offers are extended does not matter, the total number of ways to allocate the offers can be determined using the combinations formula. To find the percentage change in the number of possibilities to allocate job offers, let's compute this number before and after disqualification:

1. Before the disqualification: 6 candidates for 2 slots

Number of possibilities $= \dfrac{6!}{2!(6-2)!} = 15$

2. After the disqualification: 7 candidates (i.e. 6 - 2 + 3) for 2 slots

Number of possibilities $= \dfrac{7!}{2!(7-2)!} = 21$

Percentage increase in the number of possibilities $= \dfrac{21-15}{15} = 40\%$

78. **(E)**

Since the difference between two odd numbers must be even, the range of the set must be even, eliminating answers A and C. We also know that since each element in the set is divisible by 7, the difference between any two terms must also be divisible by 7, which eliminates choice B and D. Thus, we are left with choice E. For example, 70 could be the range of the set if the smallest and largest values were 7 and 77, respectively.

79. **(E)**

Since the driver's seat had better be occupied, we have to allocate the remaining 4 people among the 6 passenger seats. Because the order of the seat assignments is important, we will use the permutations formula: Number of passenger seat arrangements = $\frac{6!}{(4-2)!}$ = 360. This number reflects the possible arrangements for a given driver. Suppose we assigned Jake to drive. Since we can create a twin arrangement for each of the 360 cases by switching the spots of Inna and Jake (asking Inna to drive), the driver choice will double the number of arrangements: Total seat patterns = $2 \cdot 360 = 720$.

80. **(A)**

Statement (1) tells us that a clean number is an odd prime. Since 3 is the only prime number among the multiples of 3 (every other multiple of 3 will be divisible by 1, 3, and itself—more than 2 factors), this statement tells us that there is only 1 clean number among the multiples of 3 less than 100. Since we can find the number of multiples of 3 less than 100, we can find the probability to select number 3 from this set. Thus, statement (1) alone is sufficient. Statement (2) tells us that a clean number **must** be odd. Please note that this is just a necessary rather than sufficient condition and it does not mean that any odd number is clean. In other words, if a number is even, it cannot be clean, whereas if the number is odd, it may or may not be clean. Therefore, we do not have any definitive information about the definition of a clean number and cannot find how many clean numbers lie among the multiples of 3 less than 100. This statement alone is insufficient.

81. (C)

First let's compute the number of possible answer keys without the constraint on the true-false questions. Knowing that there are 2 possibilities for the correct answer on each true/false question and 4 possibilities on each multiple-choice question, we can find the total number of possible answer keys without the constraint: Number of answer keys without the constraint $= 2 \cdot 2 \cdot 2 \cdot 4 \cdot 4 = 128$. Now we need to calculate the number of answer keys that violate the constraint. These answer keys will have all "yes" or all "no" answers to the 3 true/false questions. Note that the answer to the first true/false question can be either "yes" or "no" (2 possibilities) but the remaining answers have to repeat the first, i.e. once the answer to the first question has been determined, we have only one choice for the second and third true/false answers). Since there are no restrictions on the multiple-choice questions, we still have 4 possibilities for each of the 4 multiple-choice questions.

Number of answer keys that violate the constraint $= 2 \cdot 1 \cdot 1 \cdot 4 \cdot 4 = 32$

Number of possible answer keys $= 128 - 32 = 96$

82. (D)

Let's suppose there are N students in the group of candidates. Since any candidate can be elected president, we have N choices for the first position. Because one of the people has been "used up" after we elect the president, there are N - 1 choices to select the vice president. The total number of choices for the two candidates $= N \cdot (N-1)$. Because we know that there are 90 ways to select the leaders in the committee, we can set up the equation and solve for the number of candidates N in the group:

$N \cdot (N - 1) = 90$

$N^2 - N - 90 = 0$

$(N + 9)(N - 10) = 0$

$N = 10$

Answer Key

Combinatorics Drill

1 C
2 . . . . P
3 . . . . P
4 C

Probability Drill

1 . . . . $\frac{3}{8}$
2 . . . . $\frac{1}{2}$
3 . . . . $\frac{5}{216}$
4 . . . . $\frac{5}{72}$

Lesson

1 . . . . D
2 . . . . D
3 . . . . B
4 . . . . D
5 . . . . E
6 . . . . D
7 C
8 . . . . D
9 . . . . B
10 . . . . . D
11 . . . . . E
12 . . . . . B
13 . . . . . E

Assorted

14 . . . . . . D
15 C
16 C
17 . . . . . E
18 . . . . . B
19 . . . . . D
20 C
21 . . . . . D
22 . . . . . B
23 . . . . . D
24 . . . . . E
25 . . . . . E
26 . . . . . A
27 . . . . . B
28 . . . . . A
29 . . . . . D
30 . . . . . D
31 . . . . . D
32 . . . . . D
33 . . . . . B
34 C
35 . . . . . B
36 . . . . . B
37 . . . . . A
38 C

Combinatorics

39 . . . . . A
40 . . . . . B
41 C
42 . . . . . B
43 C
44 C
45 . . . . . B
46 . . . . . D
47 . . . . . E
48 . . . . . B

Probability

49 . . . . . E
50 . . . . . A
51 . . . . . D
52 C
53 . . . . . A
54 . . . . . E
55 . . . . . D
56 C
57 C

Data Sufficiency

58 . . . . . A
59 C
60 . . . . . B
61 . . . . . B
62 . . . . . A
63 C
64 . . . . . B
65 . . . . . D
66 . . . . . E
67 . . . . . B

Challenge

68 . . . . . B
69 . . . . . D
70 . . . . . D
71 . . . . . B
72 . . . . . D
73 . . . . . A
74 C
75 . . . . . D
76 . . . . . D
77 . . . . . D
78 . . . . . E
79 . . . . . E
80 . . . . . A
81 C
82 . . . . . D